Robin Hood's Bay, North Yorkshire

DESPITE the name, there's no connection between Sherwood Forest's famous outlaw and this beautiful spot, six miles south of Whitby, located within the North York Moors National Park. That's not to say that the charming fishing village doesn't have an equally romantic past, though. The wild coastline made this a prime area for smugglers and shipwrecks and there's a wealth of stories based around the atmospheric little village. It's easy to imagine the misty winter evenings when such tales would be told around a cosy fireside.

The village appears untouched by time, and indeed, cars must be left at the top and the steep paths traversed on foot to arrive at the lower cobbled alleyways with their picturesque houses.

Walks along the coastal path allow you to explore the rugged natural beauty of the area, or you could take a guided walk around the town to hear all about the smugglers, seafarers and supernatural visitors in days gone by! ■

Dear Readers . . .

It gives me great pleasure to welcome you to "The People's Friend" Annual 2016. It's packed with great reading to keep you entertained all year round, with 25 brand-new short stories by some of your favourite "Friend" authors, all beautifully illustrated by our team of talented artists.

We also have 14 seasonal poems to uplift and enchant you, a selection of glorious watercolour paintings from the brush of J. Campbell Kerr, and a classic collection of fascinating facts and know-how from our popular "I'd Like To Know" column.

Everything in this year's Annual has been specially chosen by the "Friend" team – I do hope you enjoy reading it!

Angela

Angela Gilchrist, Editor

Contents

Poetry

p.164

p.57

J. Campbell Kerr Paintings

I'd Like To Know

You will find a classic collection of "Friend" readers' questions and answers on pages 15, 20, 45, 67, 82, 98, 122, 136, 149 **and** 167

A Time To Change

by Linda Lewis.

EDITH sat down next to Phil on the sofa and gave him a pad and a ballpoint pen. She glanced around the room, still festive with garlands and ornaments, her eye finally coming to rest on the anniversary clock on the mantelpiece.

"Right, then," she said. "It's seven o'clock on New Year's Eve. You know what that means – it's time to write our New Year resolutions."

Her husband's eyes didn't shift from the action film playing yet again on the television – how many times had he seen it now? He sighed extravagantly.

"Do we have to?"

"Of course we do," Edith replied. "We do it every year. It's like sprouts; Christmas dinner wouldn't be complete without them."

Phil pulled a face.

"I don't know why you insist on buying them. It's only your sister who eats the horrible things! The rest go in the compost."

"I buy them because it's traditional, like you watching this blessed film every year," she said with a nod towards the screen. "And like making New Year resolutions," she added, as she pulled the top off her pen. "Now, turn that off and put your thinking cap on. You know the rules: we both need to write at least five. No excuses."

Her husband frowned at the blank sheet of paper on his lap.

"Seriously, dear, I'm not sure I can think of any. Every year it gets harder to find anything I want to change. We're getting too long in the tooth."

"You speak for yourself!" Edith said with a pretence at indignation which her smile belied. "Last time I checked you were six years older than me."

They were a long-running joke, those six years.

Husband and wife settled into a companionable silence as each got busy with their thoughts. Edith found her own thoughts focusing not on a list of resolutions, but on the festive scene around her. She glanced up at the rows of cards that criss-crossed the walls. This year they'd received 68, almost as many as they'd sent out. Not that that mattered. Some of their older relatives just couldn't manage out to buy and post their cards nowadays. She liked to pick especially cheerful ones to send to them.

It had been a wonderful Christmas. The last of their visitors had gone home the day before. For more than a week the house had been filled with noise and laughter, and Edith had loved every single minute.

The living-room was a riot of colour thanks to the garlands and strands of gold and silver tinsel, not to mention the tree that had pride of place in the corner. Edith loved the way the shining baubles reflected the twinkling lights back into the room. It was a shame the decorations all had to come down soon. The house looked so bare for the first few days without them. If she had her way, it would be Christmas at least three times a year!

An idea popped into her head and she wrote something down on her pad. She glanced at Phil's pad. Still blank, and he was gazing up at the ceiling. She nudged him.

"How are you getting on?"

Phil shook his head.

"Honestly, dear, I really can't think of anything I want to change."

Edith gave his knee a gentle squeeze.

"Try harder. There must be something. It doesn't need to be anything big."

He blew out his cheeks and put the end of the pen in his mouth.

Another idea flitted into her head and she jotted down a second resolution.

"Hey! Slow down a bit. I need time to think."

"You've had the whole year!" She laughed.

Phil craned his neck, trying to take a look at her pad, but she covered it with her hand.

"No peeking!"

She levered herself up off the sofa.

"I'll get us both a sherry – see if that oils the creative wheels."

As an afterthought she picked up her pad and with a meaningful look slid it in her cardigan pocket. Phil sighed and she blew him a kiss.

A S she went to the kitchen and opened the bottle Edith found herself humming. They'd been married for more than 50 years, and were as happy today as they'd always been. Phil's hair had mostly disappeared and what he did have had gone grey years ago, plus he'd put on a few pounds round his middle. But to Edith he was pretty much perfect. She loved him just as much as she did the day they had married, maybe even more.

She poured some sherry into two small glasses, gold-rimmed ones that had been a golden wedding anniversary gift from one of their grandchildren, and took them back into the living-room.

Phil looked much happier now and she could see some jottings on his pad.

"I thought of two resolutions when you left the room," Phil said as he sipped his drink. "Thanks, sweetheart. This is just what I needed."

He sighed contentedly.

"So what do you want to do tonight? Hazel and Edward are having a party. We could always go to that. It's only at the end of the road."

"I'm happy to go if you want to, but I'm not really bothered," Edith replied. "I'd much rather stay here, watch TV, and see the New Year in with you."

Phil laughed.

"But we always do that."

"So? Do you want to go?"

"Not really," he admitted.

"Good. Then that's decided. Now, try to concentrate."

She snatched another glance at his sheet of paper. He'd written two lines.

"You need another three at least. Otherwise it's not fair."

For a few minutes there was silence apart from the ticking of the clock. It didn't take Edith very long to think of some more resolutions. They weren't big things, like trying to lose weight or giving up chocolate biscuits. They'd both tried dieting many times and always failed miserably. Seventy-four was too old to make sweeping changes.

Besides, she enjoyed baking far too much. And her husband enjoyed eating her little cakes. She always planned to freeze a batch, but sometimes half of them had gone before they were even cold.

At last Phil put down his pen and patted the pad with satisfaction.

"Finished. But it was hard," he said.

"Me, too. Right then, who's going first?" Edith asked, businesslike.

"You read them out," he said as he tore off his list, folded it like a voting paper and handed it to her.

She held up a note in each hand.

"Whose list do you want to hear first?"

He closed his eyes and stabbed his finger at one of them.

Edith put on her reading glasses and flipped the sheet of paper open, then she cleared her throat theatrically.

"Remember the rule. Neither of us can comment until I've read both lists."

Phil nodded.

"Agreed."

"Right, here we go," Edith said. "Number one: I will cut the grass once a week in the summer. Number two: I will wash the car at least once a fortnight. Number three: I will cut down on playing games on the computer. Number four: I will remember to put the bin out on a Wednesday evening. Number five: I won't forget our wedding anniversary."

She paused. Before picking up the second piece of paper, she glanced at Phil.

He pressed his finger to his lips.

"I haven't said a word."

"Good," Edith continued. "List number two. I will bake more cakes, especially date and walnut. I will only invite Maureen on Tuesdays when Phil is out playing darts. I will only watch the 'Eastenders' omnibus if I've missed an episode during the week. I will remember to put the lid back on the toothpaste. And, last but not least, I will stop buying those horrible cheap teabags."

She turned to her husband.

"There, that wasn't so bad, was it? Do you think we can stick to those?"

"I might," he said. "Although the computer games are addictive, you know."

"So I gather," Edith replied with a smile.

"How about you?" Phil asked. "Will you be able to stick to yours?"

"Probably not," she admitted. "Cutting down on soaps might be difficult."

Phil chuckled.

"You could always watch the omnibus edition while I'm down the allotment. At least, then, I wouldn't have to."

"Thanks, darling. Come here and give us a hug."

Edith snuggled up to him. Neither of them was much good at sticking to their resolutions, which was why they had made a decision a long time ago. Edith wrote her husband's New Year resolutions, and he wrote hers.

That way it didn't matter half so much if they broke them! ■

Raspberry Surprises

by Louise McIvor.

T HE ducks are skating," Auntie Helen said.

"I'm sorry?" Arlene replied, thinking that her aunt had taken leave of her senses.

"Look, the lake is frozen for about the first ten feet. The ducks are slipping and sliding all over the show, poor things."

"Oh, so they are." Arlene sipped her tea, marvelling at the way her aunt always managed to see things that other people missed.

They were in the café in the park. Arlene took her aunt out once a month for a little shopping, and the café was her aunt's favourite. It had changed hands several times – the waitresses were now called baristas and the cappuccino machine whirred away all the time.

"Just for a change, you wouldn't like to try the café on the high street?" Arlene said.

"Not at all, that's full of old people," Auntie Helen said.

Arlene spluttered into her tea. Auntie Helen was hardly in the first flush of youth herself.

"Besides, I like it here," Auntie Helen said. "I learn all sorts of things."

"Like what?" Arlene said.

"Espresso is the one in the tiny cups. It was called Turkish coffee in our day, or something like that. It's strong, so that's why the cups are so tiny."

"Is that so?" Arlene said faintly, realising her aunt was on her second cup of double espresso. "What did you have in mind today, Auntie Helen?"

Auntie Helen ignored her question.

"Come to think of it, when I married your uncle Walter, we got not one but two sets of those cups as wedding presents. They were beautiful."

Arlene listened as Auntie Helen started talking to the barista about make-up tips. That was what she loved about her auntie Helen – her endless interest in people, even though Auntie Helen did have a habit of doing everything in a bit of a rush. Auntie Helen had kindness hard-wired into her DNA.

"Do let me pay, Auntie Helen," Arlene said.

"Away on with you now," Auntie Helen said, but there was a hint of a smile on her lips, which were fuchsia pink today.

Illustration by Mandy Dixon/Thinkstockphotos.

Auntie Helen's handbag was a candy-striped affair from which she pulled out her purse, a large notebook and a bright pink pen.

"I'm looking for a pair of those patterned tights. I could be doing with a new necklace, too. The ones I have are so old-fashioned. What shade of lipstick are you wearing today?"

"I'm just wearing a little bit of lip gloss. It's sort of neutral," Arlene said.

"Neutral!" Auntie Helen snorted. "Neutral isn't going to find you a husband."

Auntie Helen regarded her niece's single status as something that could easily be overcome with the right wardrobe and good shoes, to say nothing of a wee dab of make-up.

"Husbands aren't the sort of thing you can find too easily," Arlene said. "I'm sure the right man will come along in his own good time."

"So will Christmas," Auntie Helen muttered.

Arlene wished she had gone for the double espresso instead of this rather watery tea. She needed something to fortify her nerves. Auntie Helen had always been a bit of a dynamo, as Arlene's mother would say, and age had not dimmed her enthusiasm for life one little bit. Indeed, Auntie Helen's exploits

11

as a girl – she had been good at sneaking off to dances and getting away with it – were something of a family legend.

Arlene adored her aunt, but she found keeping up with her boundless energy exhausting. However, Arlene also knew that Auntie Helen's endless round of outings was her way of making sure she stayed in touch with her favourite niece.

As Arlene listened to her aunt continuing her conversation with the barista, she thought that Auntie Helen's matchmaking was just her way of trying to see that Arlene was happy and settled. Well, she was happy, and settled in her job as a classroom assistant. But she didn't tell her aunt that sometimes she would love to have someone special in her life.

"We'd better get you out of neutral and into first gear. A visit to the cosmetics counter is in order," the older woman said, buttoning up her coat.

"No, please, Auntie Helen," Arlene said. "I am not going to have my make-up done. Last time, I ended up looking like a pantomime dame."

"Nonsense. False eyelashes suit you and the eye-shadow matched your eyes."

"Would you like a raspberry and white-chocolate scone?" Arlene asked.

"Don't change the subject," Auntie Helen said, holding up her arm for the bill.

"Look, the ducks have worked it out. They're swimming in the middle now, clever things," Arlene said, trying to distract her aunt so she could sneak off and pay the bill herself.

"So they have. But I'm still paying."

✳   ✳   ✳   ✳

At the cosmetics counter in the town's biggest department store, Auntie Helen tried to persuade Arlene to try on various bright lipsticks.

"What about this one?" Arlene suggested. She slashed the lipstick tester on to the back of her hand.

"Raspberry Surprise." Auntie Helen examined the lipstick through her reading glasses. "That's more like it. And there's a special offer on so you may as well get some nail varnish, too."

"I'll chip it," Arlene warned.

"At least get a shade that will tone with the lipstick," Auntie Helen said.

"I could try this one." Arlene picked up a shell-pink-coloured bottle. It did look rather pretty.

Next on the list was a new raincoat for Auntie Helen. All the macs in the department store were deemed "too old hat" so they ended up in a trendy boutique at the other end of the high street.

"Could you not afford laces for your shoes?" Auntie Helen asked the salesgirl.

"This is how they're meant to be, madam. They're designer shoes."

"Oh. Well, at least it saves you having to tie them."

Arlene wished she could hide in the changing-room cubicles.

"Do you not need a new coat, too, Arlene?" Auntie Helen asked as she tried on a candy-striped mackintosh which matched her handbag.

"No, I'm grand, thanks, Auntie Helen. Lunch in the park?"

"In a little while. Look, they've a sale on their scarves."

THEY surveyed their purchases as they waited for their paninis and lattes. Arlene had been persuaded to buy a silk turquoise scarf, embroidered with tiny beads around the hem.

"It was half price," Auntie Helen reminded her. "And turquoise is your colour. Look."

She unfolded the scarf and draped it around Arlene's shoulders.

"I've a dress I bought in a sale a few weeks ago. I've never managed to get anything to go with it, and I think this will look well with it," Arlene admitted. "I'm glad you persuaded me to buy it, Auntie Helen."

"Turquoise brings such warmth to your wee face," Auntie Helen said.

Arlene smiled and touched her aunt's hand briefly. No-one but Auntie Helen called her wee these days. It was nice to feel loved. Arlene put the scarf away as their food arrived as she didn't want to get mayonnaise on the delicate silk.

"Penny for them?" Auntie Helen said. "You're miles away, Arlene."

"I have another wedding to go to next week," Arlene said.

"Another one? That must be the third this year," Auntie Helen said, though not unkindly. "You're maybe thinking that it would be lovely if, one day, you had your own wedding to go to?"

"No. I can manage perfectly well on my own."

Auntie Helen stirred her latte before continuing.

"Sometimes you just have to get out there, Arlene, and not be sitting in front of the television every weekend. And when Mr Whoever does come along, don't be dilly-dallying to take your ancient aunt shopping," Auntie Helen said.

"I don't have an ancient aunt, only a very youthful one." Arlene laughed.

"Flattery will get you everywhere, dear. Now, I think it's time we hit the shops again, don't you?" Auntie Helen said, her endless energy having been recharged by the latte, panini and a watermelon juice, which she drank because she had read in a magazine that it was what all the young things were drinking.

"We never got your necklace," Arlene said.

"No, we didn't. What sort of necklace do you think I should get?"

Arlene discreetly indicated a lady at a table opposite, who was wearing a Y-shaped necklace of silver and pale glass beads.

"What about something like that?" Arlene said.

Auntie Helen put her glasses back on.

"Yes, Arlene, now you're talking. I'll just go and ask her where she got it."

Arlene watched as Auntie Helen pulled up a chair to sit beside the bewildered lady. This could take some time.

There was a row of leaflets in a rack opposite their table. Arlene had an old friend from university visiting in a few weeks' time – it would be nice to show her the sights. Arlene picked up a few leaflets about a vintage fair and a linen exhibition in the town's museum. A flyer about a concert at a nearby stately home caught her eye.

She looked at the date. It was tonight.

"You should go to that," Auntie Helen said, having finished her conversation with the necklace lady.

"I've no-one to go with," Arlene said.

"Classical concerts are the sort of thing you can go to on your own and no-one bats an eyelid. You might meet a handsome conductor. Or a pianist. Come to think of it, when I was younger I was taken to dinner by a lovely pianist . . ."

As her aunt started to reminisce about the pianist, Arlene reflected that it would be fun to have a chance to try out her new make-up and wear the yet-to-be-worn dress with her new lovely scarf.

When she got ready that night, she had to admit that the Raspberry Surprise lipstick did look rather nice . . .

That evening, mooching about the entrance hall of the stately home during the interval, Arlene bumped into someone. Literally.

"Gosh, I'm sorry. I didn't see you."

The wine had spilled down the front of her dress.

"Never mind, it's only white wine, it'll dry."

The man went to ask the waitress for some paper napkins. He handed them to Arlene, who dabbed the front of the dress.

"No harm done," she said, arranging her scarf so it covered the damage.

They got talking. Terry was neither a pianist nor a conductor but taught music at a school on the other side of town. They started comparing notes on classroom life and were so engrossed in conversation that they forgot to go back in for the second half of the concert. Though neither of them minded.

✳   ✳   ✳   ✳

Arlene and Terry got engaged a few months later, much to Auntie Helen's oft-expressed satisfaction. As neither of them were showy people, they wanted a quiet wedding followed by a reception in the town's hotel. Arlene resisted all attempts by Auntie Helen to persuade her into meringue-like wedding dresses, huge heels and elaborate hair-dos.

"What about make-up?" Auntie Helen asked, crossing off items in her notebook. "I suppose you'll make do with that neutral lip gloss again?'

Arlene smiled.

"No, Auntie Helen, I've moved from neutral into first gear, so it'll be Raspberry Surprise all the way." ■

I'd Like To Know...

Sit back and enjoy this classic selection of vintage queries from the lovely readers of the "Friend"!

Q **WE'RE** all so used to duvets nowadays that no-one remembers the layers of heavy blankets we used to have to air and clean. Where did duvets originate from? Are they European?
   – *Mrs W.P., Macclesfield.*

A **DUVETS** have been in common use throughout Europe since the 18th century. They were first used in rural Europe, and probably originated in Switzerland or Austria. The original duvets were filled with down feathers from Eider ducks, as they were well known for their insulating properties. The word duvet actually comes from the French word for down.

- -

Q **MY** husband and I were lucky enough to spend New Year with family in America a few years ago. We were very surprised to discover that the song "Auld Lang Syne" was popular there, too, and wondered why. Is it because of their Scottish heritage?

   – *Mrs S.A., Oban.*

A **THAT'S** partly true, but another reason is the band leader Guy Lombardo. He first heard "Auld Lang Syne" in his home town of London, Ontario, where it was sung by Scottish immigrants. He played the song with his brothers in his famous dance band – Guy Lombardo and His Royal Canadians – at midnight at a New Year's Eve party at the Roosevelt Hotel in New York City in 1929 and it became a tradition. Broadcast at first on radio and then on television, Lombardo's version of the song was played every New Year's Eve from the 1930s until 1976 at the Waldorf Astoria.

First Date

by Carol Probyn.

CLAIRE heard the post land on the hall floor as she sat sipping her lukewarm tea in the kitchen.

Today was Wednesday – an at-home day of ironing and listening to "Woman's Hour" a bit later. She smiled, remembering how her mother would always comment that none of the presenters would ever match up to Sue MacGregor. Dear Mum, she would certainly not approve of Claire watching breakfast TV.

She went to the door, picked up three envelopes and returned to the kitchen.

She opened the top envelope with the marmalade knife and, licking a smear from her finger, she raised an eyebrow at her credit card balance and put it to one side. Mum would be appalled! All that money on clothes!

The second envelope contained her home insurance renewal. The third envelope she had deliberately left until last, because it contained a card. She propped it up against the marmalade jar, and felt a tiny frisson of excitement. She wanted to relish its presence and ponder on its content for a while, for Claire received very few cards these days.

Last Christmas she had counted eight, including one from Paul, her new friend, and she was lucky to get four on her birthday. When Mum was alive they could usually count on a dozen from elderly members of the family, but the only ones who kept in touch with Claire were a niece and a great-nephew. The other two at Christmas had been from Sandra and Joy, her two friends. Sandra lived miles away, and she saw Joy on a Monday and Friday when they worked together at the charity shop.

Joy had a husband and a huge extended family, but valued Claire's friendship, and Claire valued hers very much. Real friends had been a rare commodity in Claire's life. She had always put her mother first. Joy was the gregarious type who lived what Claire thought of as a full life, whereas hers was like the proverbial glass, half full – or was it half empty?

She was transfixed by the envelope. Her name and address were neatly written in pen, but she didn't recognise the writing.

Perhaps it was an invitation.

The last invitation she had received was 10 years ago – an invitation to a school reunion. The thought of going had thrilled and terrified her at the same time, but she had mustered up courage and gone. There were 15 girls there, most of whom had nodded blankly when she told them she had remained single and worked as a legal assistant. She had then shrunk quietly back into her familiar role as the shy, forgotten onlooker as she listened to their strident high-pitched declarations of their successful lives.

She still received an annual e-mail invitation, but she always politely made excuses, for she had absolutely nothing in common with any of them.

"Destined to be on the shelf, you are, Claire, if you don't try harder," her mother would say all those years ago. "You can't live on memories of Stephen for ever. What's wrong with Bob from the office?"

Bob was nice, but he wasn't Stephen. Claire was relieved when he turned his attention to Muriel from accounts.

Illustration by Jim Dewar/Thinkstockphotos.

She had been engaged to Stephen for five years. It was the early Sixties and a conventional courtship, old-fashioned by today's standards, and they had spent a wonderful summer holiday together in Jersey. A month later Stephen had been killed in a car crash, and Claire had been devastated.

From then on her life had revolved around her work and her increasingly frail and dependent mother. Eventually she had to take early retirement to care for her.

"If you only got out and about more, Claire, and dressed up a bit, it might not be too late for you," her mother had said just before she died.

Claire's voluntary work and meeting Joy had been her salvation. Some of Joy's enthusiasm for life began to rub off on her.

"Sixty is the new fifty these days, Claire! That smart turquoise dress just in would suit you down to the ground. Why don't you try a smidgen of eye-shadow?"

She had, and soon afterwards she'd changed her hairdresser and purchased more new clothes in colours other than grey or beige. She told herself it was nothing to do with meeting Paul that day in the supermarket . . .

✳   ✳   ✳   ✳

She had just picked up her usual Cumberland pie for one.

"What are those like? Haven't tried them before."

A pleasant-looking gentleman was scrutinising the packaging. Claire glanced around, thinking he must be talking to someone else, but there was just the two of them. She panicked.

"I buy them for my mother," she lied. "She likes them."

She was aware that she was blushing, and reddened even more when the man met her eyes and smiled. He had nice eyes behind his spectacles, a kind face.

"Well, I'll give one a try."

Claire nodded and scurried off to the checkout. She felt quite foolish, going to pieces because a stranger had spoken to her. The truth was that it was the first time this had ever happened.

CREATURE of habit, Claire always shopped on the same day at roughly the same time, and occasionally she would see "the nice man", as she came to think of him. For many months all they did was exchange a nod or a smile, until one day he stood behind her in a queue at the checkout.

"Your mother still enjoys the Cumberland pies, I see," he said, indicating her basket.

"Actually she's passed away, but I've carried on the tradition."

They spent a few minutes exchanging opinions on the current offers and virtues of the "meals for one" range.

A month later they met again in the ready-meals aisle. This time Claire was pushing a trolley, doing a bigger than normal shop.

"Making my own Cumberland pie this weekend. A friend's coming to stay," she told him.

"Lovely!" He smiled. "I used to do a lot of cooking myself, but the joy's gone out of it these days."

He told her about losing his wife two years previously.

Perhaps she could offer to cook him a meal, she thought. But she quickly dismissed it. Whatever would he think?

It was several weeks after that when Paul invited her to join him for a coffee in the supermarket cafeteria, and now they met there most weeks. Last week he had stuttered and stumbled over the words and finally managed to suggest that she might like to join him for lunch some time at the little bistro around the corner.

Claire left the card on the table and went to shower and dress. She now looked forward to Thursdays – to seeing Paul for their weekly shop and coffee. He was almost as shy and diffident as she was, and he had recently confessed that the day he had first spoken to her in the supermarket was the first time he'd spoken to anyone in weeks. She knew how that felt. Perhaps their friendship would last. It could even develop into something stronger. Perhaps Paul's tentative suggestion and the card were connected.

She walked back into the kitchen and picked up the envelope. Well, it wouldn't open itself.

She slit it open with a clean knife and slid the card out gently. There was a simple, tasteful red heart on the front with the words *Greetings on Valentine's Day* scrolled beneath it.

Claire caught her breath. This Valentine's card was addressed to her! It was the first one she had ever received. It occurred to her that Stephen had never sent her one, but then he had been a very rational, sensible man, not given to romantic gestures. Not that it had mattered.

She sighed and closed her eyes. Dear Stephen.

CLAIRE opened the card.

Inside it said simply *To a special lady* in a flowing, cursive style she recognised from Paul's Christmas card and which bore little resemblance to the capital letters on the envelope.

She had to sit down, she felt so overwhelmed. She felt the colour rush to her face, and a little giggle escaped from her lips. She smoothed the front of the card and stared at it like it was some priceless artefact – which indeed it was to her.

The phone rang. It was Paul.

Claire felt her heart thudding in her chest like a lovesick teenager. It was a long time ago, but she recognised the feeling.

"I know it's a bit last minute, but I wondered if you'd like to come for lunch at the bistro today." He spoke very quickly, and Claire imagined him plucking up courage to say the words, dreading a negative reply.

"I'd love to," Claire said with feeling.

When she put down the phone, she placed the card in the middle of the table. She thought it was a pity her mother wasn't here to see it. She raised her eyes towards heaven.

"It's Valentine's Day, and I'm going on a date!" she whispered. ▦

I'd Like To Know....

Sit back and enjoy this classic selection of vintage queries from the lovely readers of the "Friend"!

Q **I VIVIDLY** remember a film starring Ingrid Bergman about a woman who may or may not have been the last surviving member of the Russian royal family, the Grand Duchess Anastasia. Has the mystery ever been solved of whether or not she was who she claimed to be?

– *Mrs D.S., Shetland.*

A **ACTRESS** Ingrid Bergman won an Academy Award for her starring role in the 1956 film "Anastasia". Anna Anderson, on whose claims the film was based, has since been proved by DNA evidence to be Franziska Schanzkowska, a Polish factory worker with a history of mental illness. DNA testing by the US Armed Forces DNA Identification Laboratory in 2009 proved conclusively that the remains of all four Grand Duchesses have now been accounted for, so sadly it is not possible that any of them escaped.

. . . .

Q **TRAVELLING** to visit my daughter in New York recently, I became aware that quite a few of the airports I passed through did not have gates numbered thirteen. Is this because thirteen is still considered unlucky or is there some other reason for missing it out?

– *Mrs G.J., County Durham.*

A **THE** fear of the number thirteen is so widespread that there is even a Greek term for it — triskaidekaphobia. This belief that thirteen brings bad luck has been passed down through many different societies and is still strong enough today that many major hotels and high rise buildings build only twelve floors or skip labelling thirteen altogether. Some airports do not have a gate numbered thirteen for the same reason. Not all ancient cultures feared the number thirteen, however. The Chinese and Egyptians actually thought of it as lucky.

Illustration by Marianne Vinge.

The Lost Shepherd

by Wendy Clarke.

VIOLET leaned across the pew and gave her neighbour, Rita, a nudge in the ribs.

"He's not his usual chirpy self today, is he?"

Father Peter had just finished his sermon. Something about wrestling with a serpent, or perhaps it was a servant. Violet couldn't remember exactly because she had been thinking about whether to have sprouts or cabbage with their Sunday roast when she got home.

"Maybe he's sickening for something," Rita said, moving her head to the right in order to see round Clarice Holdaway's wide-brimmed hat. "He does look a bit peaky."

"Shh." Clarice turned to glare at the two women, her oversized hat clipping

21

her husband's ear as she did so.

Violet pressed her lips together to avoid the laughter that threatened to spill out into the quiet church and nodded her apologies, relieved when Clarice turned back to face the front once more.

"Who does she think she is?" Rita hissed. "She might live up at Fairfax Hall, but the way she acts, you'd think her husband was a lord rather than someone who invented . . ." she wiggled her fingers at Clarice's broad back ". . . perfumed gloves for discerning lady gardeners."

Violet chuckled and looked beyond Malcolm Holdaway's balding head to where Father Peter was now stepping down from the pulpit. She noticed that he didn't smile at the congregation as he usually did and she was concerned to see him raise his hand, with its long, slim fingers, to his brow and pinch the soft skin between his eyes.

He had been vicar at St James's for three years and had proved to be both fastidious with his church duties and helpful when her husband Brian had had his little problem the previous year. Father Peter had recommended fresh air and bran on his porridge and, failing that, a trip to the doctor. And not once had he laughed.

Over the years after Sunday services, Violet had noticed many other villagers, after a quick glance to make sure they were not being observed, pull the vicar aside for a private word. A true leader of his flock, Violet thought.

The rest of the congregation were filing out of the church – June Collings with her three eldest boys, slouching along with their hands in their pockets, Bert Bodkins who, rumour had it, had been a wartime spy, April Jones with her pierced lip, and even old Mrs Kingsly, who must have taken the first sunny day of spring as a signal to don her stout shoes and walk the few yards between her cottage and the small Norman church. A decent turnout, she thought, and a loyal one.

As they left the church, Father Peter greeted each of his parishioners as he always did, but Violet thought his grey eyes had an unusual sadness to them. When the last of the villagers had stepped outside, he turned and walked back into the dark interior.

Violet stood, buttoning up her coat against the wind and thinking about the apple pie she had still to make, when something made her turn and look back at St James's. The heavy wooden door had not shut completely and Violet could just make out the form of Father Peter sitting in the front pew, his head in his hands. There was something about the vicar's posture that made Violet turn and slip back through the stone archway.

✱   ✱   ✱   ✱

Peter lifted his head to the altar and sighed. Ever since he had been a small boy, he had known where his path lay. After his theological studies he had spent four years as a curate in north London, where his flock had consisted mainly of the homeless seeking a warm place of rest from the elements. He remembered how happy he'd been when he had moved to Barlow Green, with its thatched cottages, picturesque duck pond and village green.

THAT was four years ago now, and during that time he had been delighted by his full church and equally full plate at the end of the service. He should have been content. But just recently he had found himself standing in the pulpit on a Sunday morning, wondering what it was all for.

The pews were full, there was no denying that, but beneath the pleasant façade of his congregation he knew that all was not as it should be in the quiet parish. Only last week old Bert Bodkins had accused June Collings's youngest of stealing one of his chickens from his back garden, and April Jones had been suspended from school for a week for refusing to wear her uniform. It was common knowledge that Clarice Holdaway, up at the big house, was refusing to speak to Rita Davies after something she had supposedly said three years before, while old Mrs Kingsly had taken to writing letters of complaint to her local MP over goodness knew what.

Peter sighed. That was not the worst of it. He looked up at the stained-glass windows that cast geometric patterns on the stone floor in front of him. The simple truth of the matter was that, two days ago, he had woken up with an emptiness inside him where his faith had once been.

"Are you all right, Vicar?" Violet sat down in the pew next to him. "It's just that you look a bit out of sorts."

Peter jumped; he hadn't heard her come in.

"Violet! Sorry, no, everything's fine."

She looked at him with raised eyebrows and Peter could see that she was unconvinced.

"You know the old saying, Vicar: a trouble shared is a trouble halved."

"Thank you, Violet, but I can assure you that I am perfectly OK."

He turned and smiled at the lady with the crocheted hat that flattened her grey curls against her head. How tempted he was to tell her what troubled him. But it was his place to soothe his worried flock, not the other way round.

He turned back to the front of the church and for a while they sat side by side in silence. When Violet spoke again, her voice was gentle.

"Tell me something, Vicar. When we have problems, we come to you." She paused, and Peter watched the candles guttering in their holders as he waited for her to continue. "Who do you talk to when something's wrong?"

"Why, God, of course."

Violet laid a hand on his arm.

"And have you talked to Him about what it is that's bothering you?"

"No. I can't," he said. There seemed no point in denying it. "That is the problem. Just recently, I have started to wonder if He is listening."

"It's natural to doubt, Vicar, we all do from time to time. You're only human like the rest of us. Give it time and I'm sure that your faith will return."

Peter looked at the stained-glass window where Jesus stood in his white robes, hand outstretched to the stormy sea.

"No, Violet," he said softly. "What I need is a miracle."

THE community hall was chilly. Violet switched on the heaters and started placing the plastic chairs in two rows in front of the small stage. "Are you sure you put the leaflets through all the right doors, Brian?" she asked.

Her husband nodded.

"Almost didn't reach old Mrs Kingsly's letter-box. Her Yorkshire terrier nearly had my ankles."

Violet laughed and looked at her watch.

"They should all be here soon."

As she spoke, the door opened and April strode in, her Doc Martens leaving muddy footprints on the wooden floor.

"Am I early?"

"No, dear," Violet said. "Take a seat."

One by one, the villagers filed into the little hall and took their seats, darting quizzical looks at one another. Violet took her seat on the stage, noticing that Rita and Clarice Holdaway had taken chairs as far away from each other as possible, and that Mrs Kingsly's terrier was chewing on the end of Bert Bodkins' scarf.

She cleared her throat.

"I expect you are all wondering why I've called this meeting at such short notice."

Folk muttered in affirmation and she went on.

"I am worried about Father Peter. Some of you may have noticed that he is not himself."

Again the villagers nodded.

"I asked him about the village fête this year and he just said that he couldn't think about it at the moment. It's not like him at all," Malcolm Holdaway said, scratching his bald head.

"Yes," June said, "and when I asked him about a spot of bother my youngest Callum has got into . . ." she glanced guiltily at Bert Bodkins ". . . all he said was, 'Another time, June'."

The community hall buzzed with voices as the villagers shared their worries about their vicar. Violet clapped her hands and the room fell quiet.

"The problem is," she said, her face grave, "that our vicar thinks he has lost

Memories

IN quiet moments, memories
Can help us through the day,
Recalling all the kindly deeds
We've met along the way.
Just time to pause can mean so much;
Refresh your mind anew,
So treasure all those memories –
They'll give new strength to you!

– *Elizabeth Gozney.*

his faith."

There was a collective intake of breath in the hall and Violet continued.

"He says he needs a miracle to get it back. So that," she said, looking at them from over the top of her glasses, "is what we must give him."

Clarice raised a hand.

"I don't know what you mean."

"I mean we must put our heads together and come up with something that Father Peter will take as a sign. Any ideas?"

June Collings's eldest boy jumped up.

"What about a crop circle? We could make a sign of a cross or something in the cornfield at the top of the village!"

"I've got a sit-on lawn mower," Malcolm Holdaway piped up. "We could use that."

Violet shook her head.

"Nobody would believe it was a miracle, Malcolm. He'd just think that kids had done it."

"Or aliens," April shouted and everybody laughed.

"What about painting tears on one of the statues in the church. It would be just like that one in Japan," Rita said, her eyes shiny with excitement. "We could use some clear nail varnish."

"No, Rita," Violet said. "Interesting idea, but we couldn't deface Father Peter's church, however much we want to help him. Any other ideas for a miracle, anyone?"

Bert Bodkins stood up and clutched his chest dramatically.

"I could pretend that I'd . . . well, you know, snuffed it, and then Father Peter could resurrect me."

There was general laughter in the hall and Violet tapped on the table with her water glass until there was quiet.

"Father Peter has been with our parish for the last four years and in that time he has been a true friend to us, turning a blind eye to our little, er, squabbles."

She watched as Rita and Clarice Holdaway shared an embarrassed smile.

"He's also lent an ear when we've needed it, and never complained when we have come to him with our little troubles."

She stared over her glasses at her husband and winked.

"Seriously, though, if we don't come up with a miracle soon, I'm afraid that Father Peter may give up the ministry and we might lose him!"

"We can't let that happen!" June called out. "He's the best minister we've ever had."

A T first, as Father Peter entered the community hall, he thought he was seeing things. Clarice Holdaway and Rita had their heads bowed over an A4 pad of paper and were scribbling furiously; April Jones and June Collings's youngest were sitting on the edge of the stage, swinging their legs and talking animatedly to Bert Bodkins. Old Mrs Kingsly, her Yorkshire terrier yapping at her heel, was loudly telling Malcolm Holdaway that what they needed to do was write a letter to their local MP, or maybe even two.

On the stage, Violet had her back to him. She stood in front of a white board and whenever one of the villagers called out to her, she wrote down what they said with a red marker.

Peter's brow creased as he made out the words.

Crop circle.

Weeping statue.

Walking on water.

A sudden gust of wind slammed the door shut behind him and Violet turned. As she saw him, her hand shot to her mouth.

Peter looked around at the groups of people who had stopped talking and were now staring at him.

"I'm sorry. Am I late?"

Violet took off her glasses.

"Father Peter! What are you doing here?"

He pulled a slip of paper out of his pocket.

"This came through my letter-box. It says '*Urgent meeting. All must attend. Eight p.m. sharp in the community hall.*' I would have come earlier only I had some pastoral duties to attend to."

He watched as Violet walked to the front of the stage and hissed at her husband.

"You didn't put one in the letter-box of the vicarage, did you, Brian?"

Her husband looked sheepish.

"Sorry, dear. Must have got carried away."

Peter looked uncomfortably around him.

"Look, I'm sorry. If I've arrived at the wrong time, I'll leave."

"No, please don't," Violet said.

She got to her feet again and addressed the villagers.

"I might as well tell him, don't you think? It was probably a stupid idea anyway."

Brian looked kindly up at his wife.

"No, it wasn't, my dear. But, yes, tell the vicar."

Violet looked at Peter and there were tears in her eyes.

"We wanted to give you a miracle," she confessed.

He raised his eyebrows in surprise.

"Give me a miracle?" he echoed.

"Yes. We thought that, if you saw a miracle in the village, it might restore your faith. We were afraid you would leave us, Vicar. Now, of course, I see it for what it was – a foolish idea."

Walking up the steps and on to the stage, Peter took Violet's hand in his.

"It wasn't foolish at all, Violet. It was generous, and very kind."

He looked down from the stage at his flock and smiled. Not the forced smile he had worn when he bade them farewell after the service that morning, but a genuine one from his heart. Snooty Clarice Holdaway, argumentative Mrs Kingsly, nosy Bert Bodkins, even troublesome little April Jones had come together, along with the rest of the villagers, just to help him.

None of them were perfect – and neither was he. He must remember that in the future.

He opened his arms wide and addressed the villagers.

"What you have done here, this evening, that is the real miracle. Thank you."

As he spoke, he knew that he meant every word. He hadn't lost his faith, just his way. And Violet, along with the rest of his parishioners, had brought him back to his true path. ■

Laxey Wheel, Isle of Man

THE Isle of Man – just 33 miles long and 13 miles wide – has quite a history. It is home to the High Court of Tynwald – the world's oldest parliament – which still legislates for the island through its two houses: the elected House of Keys and the Legislative Court. Although the Queen, as Lord of Mann, is sovereign, the island is independent and not part of the UK or the European Union.

Legend has it that the island's first ruler was the Irish sea-god, Manannán mac Lir, who would throw his cloak of mist over it to prevent detection by would-be invaders. Some say that the island owes both its name and its emblem, the triskelion or Three Legs of Man, to the god, as he was said to have had three legs on which he would roll, wheel-like, through the mist. It's a wonderful story, and the island is full of those, as belief in fairy folk runs deep here. Indeed, if you ever cross the Fairy Bridge, you must be sure to say hello to the little people to ensure good luck. ■

That Darn Cat!

by Rosie Banks.

Illustration by Jim Dewar/Thinkstockphotos.

MR WINKLES had never been what one would call a slim cat. Festively plump was the phrase that came to mind.

I maintained for years that it was nothing more than fur (because he was a marvellously furry cat), but then one day I tried to pick him up. If it was all fur, that fur was made of lead!

It had been a long winter and spring had come upon us as unexpectedly as it was welcome.

Mr Winkles revelled in the garden, keeping Bernard company among the roses, sniffing this and that, swatting disinterestedly at a passing butterfly, then reclining on the hot stones of the path and purring luxuriously.

Now that he was no longer confined to the cottage, Mr Winkles began to explore the neighbourhood in earnest. In fact, this spring he seemed more interested in it than he had been in years. He would be gone for hours on end; whole days on occasion. We encouraged him at first, believing that all the exercise would surely do wonders for his weight problem, but whatever he was doing, it was having the opposite effect. That spring, Mr Winkles was distinctly getting fatter right before our eyes!

"It's a mystery," I said to Bernard one night as we watched Mr Winkles chasing moths on the front lawn. "Look at all the exercise he's getting."

"Maybe it's all muscle," Bernard offered.

I chuckled at the notion.

"When he walks, all his 'muscle' wobbles like a jelly."

Bernard sighed.

"Oh, Margaret, you've been so tense since Shirley moved away. Let it go. Mr Winkles will be fine."

I gave him a sour look out of the corner of my eye.

"I'm just worried about him."

"You never used to worry like this."

"Well, I need to do something or I'll go out of my mind with boredom," I admitted.

SHIRLEY had been my best friend of some 30 years. We had met when Bernard and I were newly married and she and her husband moved to town. Recently her husband had retired and they had taken the opportunity to move into the city to be close to their grandchildren. I understood and respected her decision to move, but I missed her dreadfully.

I hadn't realised how close we had been until I didn't have her any more. Ours was a very small town and because I had always had Shirley, I had never taken the time really to bond with the other women my age.

Bernard had grown up in this town and I had come to love it over the years. We had no reason to move, but I had become restless.

"Margaret," he said, slipping his arm around my shoulders, "you still have me to entertain you. And Mr Winkles."

"Yes, and I'm glad and thankful," I replied, "but there's just something about a good friend who will share a cup of tea and chatter away the afternoon."

"You can always call Shirley on the telephone."

"I do, but it's not quite the same."

Bernard nodded.

"I understand."

"I suppose I'll get used to it in time," I mused.

* * * *

The veterinarian gave me a smile over the examining table.

"What have you been feeding him, Margaret?"

"That health diet food that you recommended last year!" I assured him. "He absolutely hates the stuff, but it's all he gets. I don't even give him a saucer of milk in the morning any more."

The vet stroked Mr Winkles and he purred cordially.

"It's a real mystery," the vet mused. "Somewhere, somehow, he must be accessing another food source. It's the only possible explanation."

* * * *

"None of our neighbours would feed him," Bernard mused that night at dinner.

I glanced down at Mr Winkles, doggedly munching on his diet cat biscuits by the table.

"Everyone in town knows Mr Winkles," I agreed, "and his weight problem has become an item of gossip. Mrs Bassington at the corner shop told me we should be feeding him pineapple. Apparently it worked wonders for her sister's hairdresser's Siamese."

"What did the vet say to that?"

"He choked on his tea."

"We'll give that a miss, then. What about those new people over the back fence?"

"Yes," I considered, "I'd forgotten about them."

The property that touched ours in one corner at the back had been owned for years by a delightful elderly lady who kept an immaculate garden. The garden was slowly getting to be too much work, so about six months ago she had made the decision to move into a flat on the edge of town where the garden was communal and tended by all the neighbours together. Whoever had purchased her house was reclusive. They had never come round to introduce themselves, nor did we see them at home or about the town. There was never any laundry on the line and the poor garden, once the pride of the street, was a jungle.

As the occupants of this property were an unknown quantity, I worried about dear, gentle Mr Winkles frequenting their place. I peeked out the back bedroom window at the mystery house that night, dark and foreboding, and determined to find out the very next day where it was that Mr Winkles was going on these expeditions of his.

NEXT morning Mr Winkles was out the cat flap right after breakfast. I waited until I could see him crossing the front lawn and then I ventured out behind him. Either he didn't notice me or he didn't mind, as he waddled up the street quite happily with me in tow a handful of paces behind him.

At first I was relieved. If the house I feared had been his destination, the quickest way (and Mr Winkles was an infamously lazy cat) was to access the house by cutting across our back yard. However, as we walked, I began to consider that Mr Winkles was probably too rotund to squeeze through the fence between the properties and probably would have found jumping over that fence quite an effort.

As he turned another corner, infuriating the friendly Corgi there by brushing his tail right up against his fence, I began to fear that he was simply taking the civilised way around. Sure enough, he walked me right around the block and then disappeared into the tangled front garden of the mystery house.

I was so distressed when I got home that Bernard had to bring out the lemonade.

"How could they feed him?" I asked angrily. "He's obviously not starving, and he has our address hanging right off his collar, so they must know he's not a stray. Fancy feeding him behind our backs and not even asking us!"

"Now, now," Bernard soothed, "perhaps they aren't feeding him on purpose. Perhaps there are just some bags of cat food lying around and he's got into one of them."

"Well, I'm going over there right now to give them a piece of my mind!" I told him.

Bernard watched me storm off with an affectionate twinkle in his eyes.

"Try to show a little restraint," he called to me as I went.

It was only when I had knocked smartly on the door that it occurred to me that I was, in fact, a very timid woman by nature. My protectiveness of Mr Winkles and my frustration at the loss of Shirley had conspired to give me courage, but faced with the dark frontage of the mystery house it evaporated. What on earth was I going to say?

The occupants of the house seemed to be taking a tremendously long time to answer the door. Just when I was about to give up and walk home, I heard a sound.

It was a hollow, far-off sort of sound, not unlike coins falling on a hard surface. As I strained my ears, the sound grew louder and louder. What was possessing this house? I had no desire greater than to grab Mr Winkles and leave, but my feet were glued to the spot with terror.

As soon as the door opened, Mr Winkles popped out. Seeing me, he mewed conversationally and rubbed up against my legs. I stared at the door in confusion. It opened slowly to reveal a slim woman in a cream suit.

She was a little younger than me, I judged, but not by that much. Her hair had once been blonde and she had it curled very nicely. Her face seemed kind, but it was rather hard to tell because she wore thick, dark glasses to hide her eyes. The tapping was produced by a long, white cane that swayed before her like an antenna.

"Who is it, Fluffy?" she said. "A visitor? Speak up, dear, because I can't see you."

ALICE laughed when I told her the story of how I came to her doorstep that day. She had invited me in for a cup of tea as a first priority and inside the house was cosy and well kept.

It seemed her son had landed a good job at the freezing works just out of town and she had moved down to be close to him, feeling the fresh country air would be a nice change from the city. Since moving to town, though, she had kept mostly to herself.

"But he's not overweight, surely," she mused, patting Mr Winkles affectionately. "He's just got lots of fur."

"Try to pick him up," I prompted her.

She shifted her hands from his head to his tummy and hefted him towards her lap.

"Oomph!" she said. "My word, Fluffy, you've been leading me on!"

We both laughed and Mr Winkles discreetly moved himself out of arm's reach and then resumed purring.

"I'm so sorry," Alice said, touching my hand gently. "He kept coming round and I just assumed he was hungry. Also, it was nice to have the company."

"I wish I'd known you were here," I apologised. "I would have come round and welcomed you. It's just that when we saw that no-one ever hung out the laundry and we never saw a new face about town we thought the place was deserted or that the inhabitants weren't very sociable."

Alice chuckled.

"That's understandable," she replied. "I use an indoor dryer for the washing, and my son Adam tells me the garden has fallen into dreadful disrepair. I did try attending a few community events when I first arrived, but I found the women in town to be a bit . . ." Alice sighed. "I'm sure they just don't know how to handle someone with a disability. They kept yelling things at me as though I was deaf."

"They are lovely, really, but only in small doses."

"Anyway, Adam comes round two or three times a week, but he is busy with his job, so mostly I'm just by myself. I don't mind my own company at all, but your cat was a welcome addition when he came round to visit."

"Well, he won't be the only one any more," I assured her. "Bernard can pop by and give you a hand with that garden from time to time, too."

"I would really appreciate that," Alice thanked me.

"I'm so glad I've met you, Alice," I said sincerely.

"Likewise," Alice assured me, "but is it all right if your cat still visits from time to time?"

"Of course it is!" I laughed. "But I'll give you the diet cat food that we're meant to feed him so that we're both supporting his weight loss programme."

"Meow!" Mr Winkles interjected suddenly.

"Oh, the dear boy." I chuckled. "It's almost as if he knows we're plotting against him."

"What was his real name again?"

"Mr Winkles," I replied. "It's a long story."

"My favourite kind," Alice replied. "Shall I put the kettle on again? We can make an afternoon of it." ■

Shamrock Surprises

by Pat Posner.

THIS will be the very first time you've taken me to school, won't it, Gran?"

Evelyn smiled down at her six-year-old granddaughter.

"That's because I lived too far away before. Now that I'm living just around the corner, I can take you every day."

"And," Kayla said, "I'll have to show you the way, won't I? Mummy nearly got lost the first time she took me, but we won't get lost today because I've been going there for ages and ages and I know exactly where it is," she finished breathlessly.

"I think Gran might remember where your school is," her mum said as she fastened up Kayla's blazer. "She used to go there when she was little, too."

"But wasn't it too far away?" Kayla looked puzzled, and Evelyn and Jillian laughed.

"You'll have to give her your potted history on the way to school, Mum," Jillian said. "Now off you go, or you'll be late and Bill won't still be there to see you safely over the road."

"Bill's the lollipop man, Gran. He's ever so nice."

Jillian sighed.

"We're supposed to call them school crossing patrol these days, but that doesn't sound right, does it? And the fact is," she added in a whispered aside as she opened the front door, "whatever his title is, our Kayla's got a bit of a crush on Bill."

✶   ✶   ✶   ✶

"Did you really go to my school when you were little, Gran?" Kayla asked as they walked down the road past the semi-detached houses that had been built just a few years ago.

Evelyn nodded.

"I lived round here then, Kayla, but it wasn't like it is now. There were more fields and not so many houses."

"But I know Mummy didn't go to my school, because she nearly got us lost

on my first time. Why didn't she come here, Gran?"

"Well, a little while after I got married, Gramps and I moved away to Yorkshire. That's where your mummy was born and where she went to school and to work. And that's where she and your daddy lived for a year or two, as well."

"Was I born there, Gran?"

"No. Mummy and Daddy moved to Norfolk and you were born there."

"Oh, yes, I remember. You stayed in Yorkshire and Gramps was too poorly to come to see us, so we came on long journeys to see you instead."

"You did, sweetie." Evelyn smiled.

"Then Gramps went to heaven and you came to Norfolk sometimes. And then Mummy, Daddy and me moved here and it was where you used to live. I didn't know that before. It's a bit funny, isn't it?"

Her son-in-law being offered a fantastic job here was certainly one of life's strange coincidences, Evelyn thought. That had been six months ago now.

When Jillian had suggested Evelyn move here, she'd not been too sure about coming back to the place where she'd grown up, along with the childhood sweetheart she'd married. True, they had moved away soon after; they'd lived in Yorkshire almost twice as long as they had here. But even after four years of widowhood Evelyn had been worried that walking down the Memory Lane of their youth would be too bittersweet.

"I've got good friends here," she'd said to Jillian. "I'd miss Hannah and Jessica if I moved away."

But then Hannah and Jessica had moved away to be nearer their families. So Evelyn had decided she would do the same and come to live close to Jillian, Graham and little Kayla.

In the event, the area had changed so much that there weren't too many of their "special places" left. There were two modern bungalows where the house she'd been born in used to be, though some of the old houses further along that road were still there.

The old cottage where she'd spent the first three months of married life had gone now, and a small convenience store stood in its place. Her home now – a small bungalow on a sheltered housing complex – was only a stone's throw away from where the cottage had been.

"But, Gran . . ." Kayla's piping voice interrupted Evelyn's thoughts. "Did you have St Patrick's Day when you were little and went to my school? Because that's tomorrow and I'm going to dress up as a leprechaun, and Bill the lollipop man is going to wear a shamrock on his bright yellow coat. You'll see Bill when we get round the corner. Come on, let's walk quicker."

As Kayla tugged on her hand, Evelyn smiled and quickened her pace and, sure enough, when they turned the corner, she could see the lollipop man a little way up ahead.

"Bill's on our side of the road, Gran. Can I run up to him? Mummy lets me and I won't go near the road. I won't let Bill stop the traffic until you get there."

"All right, then," Evelyn agreed.

Glancing at her watch and noting they were still in good time, Evelyn watched her red-haired granddaughter rushing along, keeping well away from the edge of the pavement.

"This is my gran, Bill," Kayla said when Evelyn joined them. "Her name is Evelyn and guess what, Bill? She used to come to this school and I don't know if she dressed up as a leprechaun on St Patrick's Day because she forgot to tell me."

"More like I didn't get a chance to tell her," Evelyn said, shaking her head.

Bill glanced at her for a long moment before looking down at Kayla again.

"I used to come to this school, too, Kayla, and I think when she was in class five, your gran dressed up as a shamrock. She wore . . ." He broke off as a small group of grown-ups and children arrived. "Excuse me. I need to stop the traffic now, Kayla," he told her.

"We'll wait and you can take us over the road next time," Kayla reasoned. "Were you really a shamrock, Gran? And how does Bill know that?"

Slightly stunned, Evelyn shook her head as she watched Bill walk into the centre of the road. Bill? William? It had to be.

"He lived about six houses away from me and my mum and dad, Kayla. Only we called him William back then. We were at this school together, in the same class! Gramps was in our class as well."

"But did you dress up as a shamrock, Gran?" Kayla demanded. "I think I would like that better than being a leprechaun. Everyone's coming as one of them."

Evelyn was too busy feeling surprised to answer. Although they had gone to different schools after taking the eleven plus exam, her parents and William's had been close friends, so she and John had still seen quite a lot of William at parties and get-togethers until he'd gone away to work in a garden nursery.

"I think the last time I saw William was at my parents' silver wedding. That was . . ." Evelyn worked out the relevant years in her head. ". . . forty-eight years ago tomorrow! They were married on St Patrick's Day. I can't think how he knows me after such a long time."

"I knew this little one reminded me of someone, Evelyn." William – or Bill as he seemed to be now – rejoined them. "As soon as she told me your name, it clicked. She's got the same red hair you used to have."

"My hair is strawberry blonde, Bill," Kayla protested loudly. "And Gran still hasn't told me if she really dressed up as a shamrock."

Evelyn laughed.

"I did, Kayla. And I'll tell you all about it when you come home from school. But if you don't go now, sweetie, you'll be late."

"Here's your boyfriend, Kayla," Bill whispered as a young lad came up. "I'll stop the traffic again and you and Joseph can cross and go into school together."

"You don't have to cross with us, Gran. Mummy stays here and watches me go through the school gate. So you can stay here and wait for Bill to come back."

Evelyn kissed Kayla goodbye and watched her cross the road with Joseph. She smiled as her granddaughter blew Bill a kiss.

I'LL be off duty in ten minutes, Evelyn," Bill said as he stepped back on to the pavement. "Have you time to come for a coffee and a catch-up? I know John's no longer with us," he added gently. "Kayla told me you were coming to live here and that her gramps was in heaven. Only I didn't know it was you, of course."

"John died four years ago," Evelyn said.

Bill shook his head.

"I've been on my own for five years now. Not a widower; Mavis and I are divorced. So, about that coffee?"

"I'll pop along to the post office and then come back. Jillian, my daughter, said they sell cotton and she wants a reel of green to finish off Kayla's leprechaun outfit. But I'd better buy some rolls of brown paper as well, because I have a feeling that Kayla will want to dress up as a shamrock instead of a leprechaun now. Thanks to you," she added with a smile.

Bill suggested going to his place for their coffee.

"I always leave everything ready to make a little snack as soon as I get back from school patrol. Besides," he added, "I want to show you something."

To Evelyn's amazement, Bill lived in the very house he had lived in with his parents.

"It came to me after Mum died," he said as he got busy making coffee and toasting currant bread. "I rented it out for years, but after my divorce I decided to come and live here myself. Partly because of the large garden. It was this garden that set me off on wanting to work with plants."

"You got a job at a small market garden here, before you moved down south to a larger garden nursery, didn't you?" Evelyn recalled.

"That was where I got called Bill. There was already a William there, so I became Bill and it stuck."

"Well, my mind seems stuck in the past at the moment," Evelyn admitted. "Wasn't it the small market garden here where you got . . . ?"

"Twenty-five shamrocks for you to wrap in silver paper for your parents' silver wedding." Bill finished the sentence for her. "Though I only managed to get twenty from the market garden. The other five were large clovers from my own garden."

"And Dad caught us putting them in pots. When I said there was one shamrock for every year he and Mum had been married he said we'd call them Shamrock Surprises, because he'd bought Mum an eternity ring and a silver bracelet with a leprechaun charm. He decided to hide them in two of the little pots."

They continued to chat about old times, their marriages – and Bill's divorce – and of more recent happenings as they sat at the kitchen table with their drinks and toast. When they'd finished their second mug of coffee, Bill stood up.

"I said I wanted to show you something. You'll have to come into my garden shed."

Evelyn smiled when she saw the rows of shamrocks in tiny pots lined up on the work bench.

"Returning here brought all sorts of memories back. It was remembering

Signs Of Hope

WHAT do they tell you, the signs all around:
The shoots bravely budding in dark, dampened ground,
When winds are still blowing, grey skies threaten snow,
And spring's long in coming so spirits are low?
That just like the daffodils longing to bloom,
Hope's stirring and pushing its way through the gloom,
So press on regardless, have courage and smile,
Though plants are still sleeping, they'll wake in a while.
Then suddenly you'll find that spring's in the air,
Your heart filled with sunshine and flowers everywhere!

– Chrissy Greenslade.

what we did for your parents' silver wedding that made me think of this, Evelyn. It's not twenty-five Shamrock Surprises, though, there are just twenty-four. They're for the over-sixties' St Patrick's Party tomorrow night. There's a little surprise hidden in each one. Sweets or a tiny chocolate bar wrapped in green paper."

"That's a lovely idea." Evelyn laughed.

"I did it the first time four years ago when I noticed my shamrock plants had multiplied amazingly. I only intended it to be a one-off for that year, but it was so successful that I have done it ever since.

"If you'd like to come to the party, I could easily dig up another shamrock and put it in a pot for you," he continued. "What a coincidence that would be – you, me and twenty-five Shamrock Surprises, together again after all these years."

Evelyn smiled.

"I would love to come. I'll wear Mum's leprechaun bracelet, in fact. I've got her eternity ring, too, but I've put that away to give to Kayla when she's a bit older. Speaking of Kayla, in case she does want to be a shamrock tomorrow I had better get back to Jillian's now and convince her that turning Kayla into one will be quite easy."

Bill nodded.

"Trousers made from brown paper to look like earth, and a green fabric shamrock on her back and front – and you mustn't forget a circlet of shamrocks for her red – sorry, strawberry-blonde – curls." Bill chuckled. "All these years and I still remember you looked amazing. And Kayla will, too, if she decides to be a shamrock.

"We had better pick a few more from my garden for you to take with you, Evelyn. Even if Kayla sticks to being a leprechaun, she could carry them in a little basket."

IT'S such a shame, William – Bill, that is – and Mavis didn't have a family," Evelyn said to Jillian after she'd told her all about her morning with Bill. "He obviously loves children."

"It wouldn't surprise me if you and he were to start spending time together, Mum. And if you do, Kayla will probably want in on the act. As I told you, she's got a bit of a crush on him," Jillian added, laughing.

"I'll be seeing him tomorrow evening at the party," Evelyn told her daughter. "We'll see how that goes before deciding if we'll be spending more time together."

"Right now," Jillian said, "I'm guessing Kayla will want to be a shamrock tomorrow. So how about you making her outfit? If it's as easy as you say, you'll have it finished by the time she gets home from school. It'll be a nice surprise for her."

"A Shamrock Surprise," Evelyn said, smiling.

✳   ✳   ✳   ✳

Evelyn smiled on the evening of St Patrick's Day, too, when her surprise in the shamrock Bill presented to her was a bright green envelope containing two tickets for a play at the local theatre.

"You mentioned that you'd like to see it," Bill explained. "So I thought we could maybe go together."

"I think I'd like that very much, Bill," she replied. ▐

Illustration by Mandy Dixon/Thinkstockphotos.

What Really Matters

by Samantha Tonge.

HIS heart pounding, Tim set his jaw firmly and started to run as fast as he could. With the frying-pan in his hand, he tossed its contents into the air, higher than he had meant. As the pancake fell on to the grass, Tim giggled with nerves. He bent down to pick it up and glanced across to the sidelines. His dad was standing there with a big grin on his face as he saw the mishap. He gave his son the thumbs-up.

At that moment Benny Brown hurtled past. Mr Brown, Benny's dad, was shouting from the finish line, hollering at Benny to run as fast as he could.

Tim felt sorry for his friend. Mr Brown had promised to take Benny to the burger bar afterwards – but only if he won. This was a special treat, as Tim knew Benny's dad didn't like the place. But Benny had told Tim they'd been given a special discount card, so his dad had relented. But only if he won . . .

His feet moving again, as he ran past, Tim had time to notice the look of concentration on Mr Brown's face; it was as if his life depended on his son winning the race!

In the event, Benny came second, while Tim trundled in fifth – with a very muddy pancake after dropping it twice more. Unlike Benny, who hadn't

41

dropped his pancake once. His was pristine.

"Bad luck, son." Tim's dad was waiting for him at the finish line and clapped him enthusiastically on the back. They caught each other's eye and started to laugh. "Perhaps we should have spent a bit more time actually practising tossing pancakes, and less time just eating them!"

"No way!" Tim argued. "Those chocolate ones last night were yummy!" He gave his dad a quick hug.

"Didn't you put in much training, then, Tim?" Benny asked in a small voice. With mouth down-turned, he was standing nearby, waiting while Mr Brown stowed their frying-pan in a bag.

Tim sensed his friend's disappointment and gave him a half-smile.

"No. I don't like running. But you ran faster than Usain Bolt, Benny! I did my best, but Dad told me we should make the practices fun. So he spent most of the evenings this week teaching me how to make pancake batter and cook it, didn't you, Dad?"

"Aren't you interested in winning, though, young Tim?" Mr Brown broke in, shaking Tim's dad's hand and looking down at the two boys.

"Hello, Don, long time no see. Actually, I've taught our Tim that it's the taking part that is most important, not coming first," his dad said mildly.

Mr Brown rolled his eyes, his lips tight.

"That old chestnut, eh? Well, all I can say is it never made me feel better as a lad when, year in and year out, I came last in the school sports events."

At that moment Tim's dad spotted Mrs Jones, a mum who ran the school's parents' committee.

"Each to their own," he said to Mr Brown, and winked at Tim. "I'll be back in a moment. I want to see if they need my help organising the spring fair."

BENNY and Tim sat down on a tree trunk to wait, whilst Mr Brown busied himself with his mobile phone.

"I'm going to miss pancake-racing when we go to high school next year," Tim said brightly. He glanced sideways at his friend, whose shoulders were slumped.

"I'm not," Benny muttered with a quick glance up at his dad. "I wish my dad was more like yours, Tim. I try my best, I really do, but Dad takes any competition so seriously. It was only a pancake race! And football is no fun any more since I got into the team. It's good that Dad comes to watch me play, but all he ever does is try to give me tip after tip – he even shouts them at me from the crowd during the match." He brushed his hair out of his face and met Tim's gaze with damp eyes. "It's dead embarrassing."

Tim stole a look at his friend's father, who seemed to be concentrating hard on his phone's screen. For a second Tim thought he might be listening to the boys' conversation . . . But no, he probably just had some really important text

TV Talk

I SWITCH the television on,
A programme I must see,
But there they sit, all side by side,
To talk to you and me.
There could be sport, exciting bits,
Yet still more talk I hear.
Presenters, can't you go away?
I wish you'd disappear!
So then I change the channel –
The adverts talk and shout.
There are so many, I forget
Just what the film's about!
At last I switch the TV off –
I think it's time for bed.
Tomorrow I will take a walk
And talk to trees instead!

– *Iris Hesselden.*

to check.

"Why do you reckon your father is like that?" Tim asked quietly.

Benny picked a long blade of grass. He twisted it around one thumb and then tossed it away.

"I reckon it's because he never won any sports or races when he was at school. He says it used to make him feel bad, even though he was the best in his class at English and Maths."

"But so what if he lost some races?" Tim asked, his brow furrowed. "Why does it matter now? He has a really important job, you said."

"Yeah, he's just been made a partner or something." Benny's chest puffed out a little. He was obviously proud. "Mum says his boss is dead pleased with him. He reckons he is good in court, helping people who have been accused of things they haven't done."

"So why does he care so much about a stupid pancake race, then? I don't understand!" Tim raised his arms and let them drop.

Benny sat silent for a moment, thinking.

"I think that coming out on top has always been really important to him. I mean, he chose a job that's all about winning or losing. But I'm not my dad!" Benny's voice carried a slight tremble again. "I mean, don't get me wrong, it's nice to win. But as long as I know I've done my best, well, I'm happy."

Tim nodded in agreement.

"My dad never won anything when he was a kid, either. But he always says that what happens at school doesn't often have much to do with grown-up life." Tim's eyes widened. "Now I think of it, my dad was always in trouble for bunking off and not doing his homework!" He laughed.

"Really?" Benny's head lifted.

"Yep. He showed me his Year Six school report once. It said he'd never amount . . . amount . . . well, I can't remember the exact words, but the headmaster didn't think Dad would ever get a good job!"

"And now your dad runs his own plumbing business. That shows all they knew back then!" Benny laughed a little, then shrugged. "I guess my dad means well . . ."

He broke off as Mr Brown cleared his throat and put his mobile phone in his pocket, but he was still paying little attention to the boys.

"I think my dad does wish he had tried harder at school," Tim carried on. "And he would never approve of me getting in trouble or skipping school. But I reckon Dad's right, really. School days are school days, and most people just leave them behind."

"That's just as well, looking at your latest haircut," Benny teased, his eyes brighter.

Tim punched him on the arm, pleased to see his friend had cheered up a bit.

Mr Brown cleared his throat again and looked down at them both.

"Come on, lads." He fiddled with the strap of what looked like an expensive watch. "Tim, let's catch up with your dad. Perhaps the four of us could go and get a burger for tea. After all, seeing as how you two lads, well . . ." His voice became uneven. "Second and fifth positions are decent enough, in my opinion. I'm proud of you both."

Benny's jaw dropped.

"Really, Dad? But what about football practice tonight?" Benny turned to Tim. "I've a big match tomorrow morning, and normally on a Friday night Dad takes me jogging around the park."

Mr Brown stared at the two boys for a moment and Tim noticed a lump move in his throat as the man swallowed. He looked away from them and into the distance.

"I guess it won't matter if we miss one night's training, Benny. And after all, it would be a shame to waste that discount card. Go on, now. You two get changed whilst I find your dad, Tim."

As the boys walked across the grass towards the school buildings, Tim nudged his friend.

"Beat you to the changing-rooms!" he said.

Benny glanced at his dad for a second, as if expecting him to offer some tips. But Mr Brown just smiled. Benny smiled back and then, shouting with glee, he and Tim started to run. ■

I'd Like To Know...

Sit back and enjoy this classic selection of vintage queries from the lovely readers of the "Friend"!

Q **WHY** are wedding and engagement rings worn on the left hand? I wear my engagement ring first on my finger and then my wedding band because that is the order in which my husband gave the rings to me. My friend says that this is wrong and my wedding band should be under my engagement ring. Which one of us is right?

– Mrs C. G., Canterbury.

A **WE** wear wedding rings on the left hand in this country, Mrs G., but in many other countries, e.g. Germany, Greece, Poland, Norway and Spain they wear them on the right hand. After the wedding a wedding band is traditionally worn first on the finger with the engagement ring on top of it, but it is really a matter of personal preference and the style of the two rings.

- -

Q **WATCHING** "Dad's Army" on TV recently has started a debate between my friend and myself. We were trying to remember the main characters' names, but have forgotten what the dour Scotsman and the ARP warden were called. Can you help?

– Mr W.D., Doncaster.

A **PRIVATE JAMES FRAZER**, played by John Laurie, was the dour Scotsman and the ARP warden was William Hodges, played by Bill Pertwee. The BBC sitcom ran for nine series and eighty episodes in all and was broadcast between 1968 and 1977. It still ranks today as one of Britain's best-loved sitcoms.

Q **IT** is, without a doubt, one of the UK's best-known and much-loved books, but can you tell me if "Black Beauty" by Anna Sewell is based on a true story?

– Mr R.T., Cheshire.

A **WITH** fifty million copies sold, "Black Beauty" is one of the bestselling books of all time. Written in 1877 by Anna Sewell, it was her first and only novel. Although not based on a true story, she said that she wrote it "to induce kindness, sympathy, and an understanding of the treatment of horses."

Illustration by Jim Dewar/Thinkstockphoto

Easter Trees

by Jean Cullop.

O N Good Fridays Brown Owl had always taken the Brownies to the park to allow their parents time to attend church. For Triss Jenkins those had been special days; happy and sunny.

At Brownies, if Triss made mistakes it never seemed important, and this gave her the confidence she needed to try new things; confidence she didn't have at home, where her loving, caring, well-meaning but over-ambitious parents were anxious for her to succeed.

The children sat beneath the fresh green leaves of the plane trees while Brown Owl read them the Good Friday story, then they sang "There Is A Green Hill Far Away" and said a short prayer.

"We won't go to the swings," Brown Owl would say as they gravitated towards the play area. "You see, Good Friday is a sad day. We shall go for a walk instead and look at all the beautiful things around us in our world."

So they walked through the park in twos with Brown Owl naming interesting trees or birds or flowers.

On Easter Sunday the Brownies went to church, and that was a happy day with music and Easter eggs for the children. The church was filled with flowers.

Triss had loved Easter Sunday ever since and she had loved spring flowers, but a lot of water had passed under the bridge since then and right now, colourful flowers and music were not what Triss desired. What she needed was some quiet time to sort out her muddled thoughts. She had hoped that the contemplative Good Friday service would help her.

So when, after a busy morning delivering Easter eggs to her grandchildren, she hurried to church, only to find that the door was locked, she was stumped.

There was a notice pinned on the door.

"Oh, no, it can't be!" she exclaimed in dismay.

The new vicar had decided the service should be moved to the evening so that people who had to work on Good Friday could attend.

There was no way she could come tonight as she must be at the hospital for visiting time. Unsure what to do next, she continued to stare at the closed door, a petite figure whose neat appearance masked her inner confusion.

If only Steve were here. But her husband not being here was the very reason she was upset in the first place.

TRISS decided there was no point in standing here any longer, but she was reluctant to go home to an empty house. She hated the emptiness. She hated the hollow echo of her steps on the wooden floors. She hated seeing Steve in a hospital bed. He was the strong, capable one in their marriage, and now suddenly he was weak and she had to take over his role.

There were a hundred things to organise before he came home, and Triss needed to catch her breath before making a start on them.

At home, too, memories would have distracted her. Happy memories, but not what she needed today.

What could she do on Good Friday? Maybe she could find another church?

Suddenly she remembered the place where she had been taken as a Brownie. It was a special place of fresh air and birdsong; of spring flowers and new green leaves. Today she would return to the place she called Easter Trees.

The park was just a short walk from the church, and with butterflies dancing and fluttering in her tummy, Triss walked the well-remembered path down a grassy hill through a tunnel of trees, already bright with new foliage.

"If Good Friday is a sad day, no-one has told the weather," she said to nobody in particular.

It was a glorious spring day; the flower-beds blazed with flowers, their heady scent everywhere. The last of the daffodils danced in the breeze and the sun shining through the branches of the trees dappled the grass in light and shade.

The wooden park bench was still there. Triss sat down, thankful they hadn't replaced the bench with a new plastic one.

She pictured Brown Owl resting here while her Brownies sat on the grass at her feet, and for a split second Triss had the impression that the shy little girl she had once been still danced happily through the trees.

Her thoughts ran on unchecked. Where was Brown Owl now? What did the Brownies do?

Never mind the Brownies – what should I do, she asked herself.

She had good friends, but few people understood how it felt to be cut adrift from one half of her life. Steve was her rock; she never had to worry about practical things like putting out the recycling on the right day or making sure everywhere was safe at night. Now she was responsible and it felt lonely.

Steve had done way beyond anything even her children could understand, because from the moment they met and all through the years he had been her encourager.

Her parents, both high achievers, were anxious their only daughter should shine. When she failed to meet their standards she sensed their disappointment and her confidence gradually eroded.

Steve changed that. He gave her self-assurance to learn to swim, to help with reading at the local school, to return to work after their two children were independent, and most important of all, to believe in herself.

"You're as good as the next person, Triss." Sitting here, she could almost hear his voice. "Not any better, nor worse. Don't let folk tell you differently."

But in the flash of a massive heart attack she had lost her self-belief, along with her rock, and she needed to find both again.

"I need help from somewhere," she whispered. It was the closest she could get to a prayer right now and her only reply was the rustling of the trees.

When a middle-aged lady sat next to her, she did her best to pretend her companion wasn't there.

"It's a glorious day, isn't it?"

This lady didn't intend to be ignored. She had the sort of face you would find easy to talk to, only Triss didn't want to talk.

"It's quiet here," she replied pointedly.

"It was quiet before I arrived." The woman laughed. "My name's Ruth."

"Triss." She knew her voice was stilted.

Sharing her troubles with a stranger was the last thing Triss wanted, yet suddenly she found herself recounting them to a woman she had never met before. She told Ruth about Steve's heart attack, how her life was turned upside-down, and what confidence she had being shattered.

"It's not fair! Why would God do this to a good man like Steve?" she asked.

"I don't think it works like that," Ruth replied quietly.

"It does!" Triss cried, sounding petulant even to her own ears. "My Steve will never be the man he was! I don't know how we're going to get about without him to drive!"

"It's tough," Ruth agreed. "Life changes can be terribly hard, and no-one quite realises how much there is to do at these times."

"If only I could have gone to church," Triss said lamely.

Ruth ran her hand down the trunk of the nearest tree. Silver bark crumbled and came away in her palm.

Triss stared at it.

"It looks dead. Is the tree diseased?"

"No. Plane trees are like that. The bark often crumbles away, but I wonder how many years the tree has stood here and why it hasn't died?"

"Is it because it's strong underneath?" Triss asked slowly.

Ruth nodded.

"The outer covering may look as though it's damaged, but beneath that the tree is solid and healthy. Your way of life has changed, Triss, but other things are waiting for you – better things."

Triss didn't reply.

RUTH touched her hand.

"Look, I have an appointment I can't miss, but can I leave you my card? Get in touch with me when you feel you're ready. I wish you well."

Triss didn't reply, though she suddenly thought of lots she wanted to say.

She considered what Ruth had told her. Steve was still Steve; he just couldn't do some of the things he used to. Just thinking rationally calmed her until she was able to bathe in the peacefulness of the surroundings and draw strength from what she had learned.

Sitting here felt like being in church. The tunnel of plane trees formed a vaulted nave, the sun filtered through their branches like stained-glass windows and the soft, rustling breeze offered up a gentle song of praise.

After the pain of Good Friday, the joy of Easter Sunday brought hope to the world. In her mind she heard Steve whisper with the trees.

"You can do it, Triss."

Her lovely husband would soon be coming home. She needed to stay positive for both of them. There were so many things to organise, but she would tackle them one by one.

But how would they get around without transport? Driving was the one thing he had never given her the confidence to overcome. Changing gear confused her most of all.

Curiously she glanced at the business card Ruth had given her. *Silver Driving School – lessons for the over-fifties. Progress at your own pace with our patient, experienced instructors. Manual and automatic cars.*

Laughter bubbled within her. Today was Good Friday, but Easter Sunday was not far away and God had a funny way of answering prayers, sitting here in the place Triss called Easter Trees. ■

Illustration by Mandy Dixon/Thinkstockphotos.

Father's Pride

by Christine Evans.

I DON'T know what you will all do when I'm gone!" Michael moaned, wielding a spanner. "It's 'Dad, can you do this?' and 'Dad, can you do that?' And that's just the girls! You're as bad. It's always 'Michael, dear' when you want something. You all take me for granted."

Aileen was passing with an armful of newly pressed ironing and caught most of the grump. Oh, dear, her husband really was down in the dumps! He'd had a milestone birthday a couple of months before and, to her surprise, he'd been really affected by it. But then, nobody liked to be reminded by the calendar that they were getting older.

She stooped and kissed the top of his head as he bent over the bicycle tyre.

"Welcome to Mum's world," she said, laughing. "Being taken for granted is a way of life for us mums. After all, when did you last thank me for doing the washing and ironing?"

Her husband looked shamefaced.

"I didn't really mean you, love," he apologised humbly. "It's mostly the girls. When I tell the lads at work that I've got three daughters, they say I must be spoiled rotten in a house full of women. Some hopes, I tell them. I'm just the general dogsbody round here. The go-to guy when something goes wrong or they want to borrow money."

"My, my, you have got it bad!" Aileen laughed. "Would you like a cup of tea?"

Michael nodded.

"Please."

"Lindsey?" Aileen called her youngest daughter. "Make your dad a cup of tea."

"Aw, Mum!" Lindsey groaned. "I'm just about to go and meet my mates in the park when Dad's mended my puncture. I've got to get ready yet."

"That's all right," her mother said sternly. "I'll just tell your father to stop mending your bike so he can make his own tea. Or perhaps I'll stop doing the ironing and you can do your own shorts and top for going out with your friends to the park."

"All right, then." Lindsey sighed loudly.

Minutes later, Angie, their middle daughter, burst in with a couple of designer carrier bags.

"Dad, I've just bought this divine handbag. It was a bargain and it would have been gone by next week. I don't suppose you could lend me a few quid until I get paid?"

Aileen shook her head. Despite all her efforts to get Angie to live within her means, her daughter was always needing to borrow a bit before she was paid.

"The Bank of Mum and Dad again?" He sighed. "I thought we had brought you kids up with more sense. You don't know you're born! In our day you saved up and then bought the handbag."

"I didn't know you used a handbag," his daughter countered with a cheeky grin.

"Don't sauce your father," Aileen said with a barely suppressed chuckle.

Poor Michael. He was the butt of all their little jokes. He really was feeling got at these days.

Aileen remembered it was Father's Day soon. There had been signs in the supermarket reminding people to buy gifts and cards for their dads and grandads. A Father's Day card display had been moved to a prominent place in the store. But she couldn't for the life of her remember when it was. All she knew was that the girls hadn't mentioned anything. Usually they asked her if there was anything Michael needed or wanted.

"Waste of money," he'd say every year, protesting that Father's Day was an American gimmick invented by card manufacturers.

Despite his protests, though, Aileen knew he was always secretly pleased when the girls remembered to give him a little something, especially when his daughters made something for him themselves, and she always encouraged them to do so. He proudly displayed their home-made cards for over a week. But she was sorry he was feeling so neglected at the moment. He would be hurt if they forgot or didn't give him a card, at least.

* * * *

Aileen decided to have a word with Katie, her eldest daughter. Katie had married Des a couple of years before and Aileen still missed her cheerful presence around the home. She was the sensible daughter, the one who kept her younger sisters in check and maintained the peace between them.

Aileen gave her daughter a call on the phone. After some small talk she came to the point.

"I know Father's Day is coming soon, though I'm not sure when it is. You won't forget, will you? I think your dad's feeling a bit undervalued nowadays. Perhaps you could make a fuss of him."

"Don't worry, Mum. I know Dad's been a bit down since his birthday. It doesn't help that we keep teasing him about it. But don't worry about Father's Day, it's all in hand. I reminded the girls about it the other day and we've got a few ideas."

Aileen knew she could rely on Katie. But she saw no unusual activity from her other two daughters or any dropped hints. Angie was always short of money and habitually borrowed from Aileen to buy her father's gift. Lindsey usually made something as she was good at handicrafts and never had much money, either. Then Aileen began to notice giggling behind closed doors and stuff being hurriedly squirrelled away whenever she knocked and entered. She knew something was afoot.

Luckily, her husband was oblivious to any plotting.

A S the sun rose on Father's Day there came a loud knock on the bedroom door.

"Room service!" one of the girls called, which was followed by a lot of giggling.

"Are you decent?"

"Come on in," Aileen shouted.

"Happy Father's Day!" the girls shouted as they bustled into the bedroom.

As she and Michael struggled to sit up, Lindsey and Angie arrived, full of smiles. Angie was carrying a tray and her sister followed with one of their small occasional tables, a teapot and some mugs.

Lindsey put down the table and dashed off again downstairs. Minutes later she arrived back carrying the toaster, which she plugged into a wall socket.

"A toaster?" Aileen asked, surprised.

"We know Dad likes his toast piping hot and soggy with butter, so we're going to make it fresh when you've eaten the rest of your breakfast," she explained with a grin.

"Great idea. I can't abide cold, rubbery toast," Michael said. "This is a nice surprise, girls. Very thoughtful."

"You've thought of everything, but don't get crumbs all over the carpet," Aileen warned, smiling at their ingenuity.

The tray had a wire stand on each side and Angie pulled them down and arranged the tray in front of her father. There was a bowl of steaming porridge, his favourite honey and a tangy glass of orange juice. She lifted up a covering plate to reveal a plate of bacon and eggs underneath with all the trimmings – tomatoes, mushrooms, black pudding and fried bread. Then she popped it down again to keep the food warm.

"Only the best for our dad!"

Michael preened himself.

"You won't be left out, Mum," Angie added as her sister disappeared downstairs again. "Lindsey's bringing yours in a minute. But Dad gets served first because it's his day."

Michael smirked at Aileen and thumbed his nose.

"How about this, Aileen? A millionaire couldn't get better service," he said. "Well done, girls."

Aileen was so pleased that they'd gone to so much effort for their father. Her husband was certainly enjoying the fuss as his daughters flitted round him, pouring fresh tea and buttering toast. Then they sat on the bed, drinking tea and eating toast after they'd served Aileen.

When they'd cleared the trays away they brought a bag of goodies for their father.

"You shouldn't have done all this, girls," Michael protested, but looking pleased all the same. "Father's Day is an American invention by . . ."

"We know all that, Dad," Angie interrupted impatiently. "Just open your pressies."

He took out the envelopes first from the heavy bag. They'd written him a couple of funny cards that made him laugh, scrupulously avoiding jokes about his age. The weight was caused by a selection of real ales, and there was a book of recommended pubs that served meals, too.

"What's that in one of the pages?" Aileen asked.

Michael opened the book at the page and saw a hand-tooled leather bookmark with *Best Dad In The World* painted on in beautiful gold script. It was obviously one of Lindsey's efforts and they all thought it was gorgeous.

"Look at that page," Angie explained. "That's the pub we're going to for lunch as Katie's treat. She's calling for us all at twelve o'clock, so we have to be ready, as it will be crowded today and they won't hold the reservation if we're late."

"You've gone to a lot of trouble, girls. This is brilliant!" Michael said. "But I hope you can afford it all."

"We've been saving," Angie said.

"Saving!" Michael and Aileen cried in surprise.

"Well, I never thought I'd hear that from you two," Michael said, his eyes opened wide in amazement. "It's as good as a present itself to hear that."

"Perhaps what we've tried to teach them has sunk in after all," Aileen said, laughing.

"This is a day of wonders," Michael said, shaking his head. "Anyway, off you two go and let your mum and I get ready."

The girls went off giggling and when their parents arrived downstairs the kitchen was spick and span, which surprised Aileen no end.

THEY were all ready in their best clothes when Katie and Des arrived. "Happy Father's Day, Dad," his eldest daughter said, giving her father a kiss and a hug.

"Cheers, Michael," Des said, shaking his hand warmly.

They were accompanied by Des's mother. Nora was a widow and seemed very apologetic.

"I told them I shouldn't come with you all, as it was Father's Day and it was Michael's treat," she told them. "I didn't want to intrude, but Katie and Des insisted I come, too."

"You're more than welcome, Nora," Michael said, kissing her cheek. "This is a family celebration and you're family."

She looked relieved at her warm welcome.

After a pleasant country run, with Aileen driving so her husband could have a drink, the pub they came to was old and full of character, just as the girls knew their father liked. There were low beams, inglenooks and horse brasses to add to his delight.

"This is grand," he told his beaming daughters.

"They've gone to a lot of trouble to find this place," he murmured to Aileen. "I hope they can afford it. You know Father's Day is . . ."

"A wonderful day to show their dad how much they think of him," Aileen said firmly. "And you should just soak up the fuss and enjoy it. Tomorrow you might be back to being ignored!"

Although the pub was crowded and the service was a little slow because of the day, the family had a lovely meal and there was more time to chat between the courses. Full of good food and good cheer, they returned home.

Michael couldn't thank them enough for the lovely time he'd had.

The Great Escape

A BOOK is so much more than printed words upon a page;
The words are mighty characters; the book an endless stage.
So when I need a lift I always find a cosy nook
To snuggle up and wander through the pages of a book.

Transported by the written word to any time or place,
You'll find imagination is as limitless as space.
So when you feel dejected then you'll know just where to look
To find a great escape between the covers of a book.

– Dennis Turner.

"I couldn't have asked for a nicer day," he said.

"It's not over yet," Katie said, hugging her father.

MICHAEL'S daughters ushered him into the house and made him sit with his feet up. Then they poured him a glass of his favourite beer and put his favourite John Wayne movie in the DVD player for him.

"Are you all right with this, Nora?" Michael asked their guest, ever mindful of hospitality.

"You go ahead and enjoy it, Michael," she said. "I'm partial to a good western myself."

They all settled down to watch the film, but it was halfway through when he began to nod and gently snore. Aileen beckoned, and the family tiptoed out into the garden and left him in peace with the gunfire echoing round him!

Aileen was serving an afternoon cup of tea when Michael came out into the garden, stretching himself.

"I must have nodded off," he said. "It's all that good food."

"And good beer," Lindsey teased.

"Sit down and I'll make you a fresh cup of tea," Aileen said, but Angie stopped her.

"We'll do it, Mum," she said, beckoning Lindsey to help her.

Aileen was surprised by the enthusiasm of her daughters. It usually took a lot of coaxing for them to make a hot drink.

✳ ✳ ✳ ✳

Finally, as they all sat round the patio table, Katie stood up. She held out her hand to Des.

"We've got another surprise for you," she said, smiling. "It's one of the reasons we wanted Nora to be here, too. Will you tell them, Des?"

Des took Katie's hand and, smiling lovingly at his wife, turned to face them all.

"Michael, soon you're not the only one who'll be a daddy," he said with a grin.

"You mean . . .? A baby – brilliant! I'm going to be a grandad!" Michael whooped, full of delight. He grabbed Aileen's hand. "Oh, heck, though. I'll be married to an old granny!"

Aileen punched his arm playfully.

"Cheeky devil! But, you two, I'm so pleased! Congratulations," Aileen said, hugging her daughter in all the excitement.

Michael kissed his daughter, too, and then held her at arm's length as if she were made of porcelain.

"My little girl, a mother! I can't believe it."

The girls were thrilled they were going to be aunties and Nora shed tears of joy as she hugged Katie and Des.

Michael turned to Des and warmly shook his hand.

"I couldn't be more pleased for you." He put a fatherly hand on his son-in-law's shoulder. "But you do know what this means, don't you? A word of warning. If it's a girl, you'll be putty in her hands. She'll be able to wrap you round her little finger. I know from bitter experience. I've got three of 'em and they run me ragged. No wonder I'm prematurely grey and broke."

He turned to his three daughters with a grin.

"But you know what? I wouldn't be without them for the world."

His girls all cheered him.

Aileen hugged her husband, knowing his previous cloud of gloom was well and truly dispelled. What a difference the wonderful day and the wonderful news had made. For weeks Michael had been depressed by his creeping age, but now he was going to be a grandad and married to an "old granny" he was on top of the world!

And in the mêlée of a group hug, she knew at that moment he was the proudest man on earth. ▪

Norwich

PICTURESQUE Norwich has been successful in retaining the charm of its ancient past while adapting to the requirements of modern life. Amid the cobbled streets, Norman cathedral, mediaeval castle and historic 900-year-old market is a vibrant, bustling city. It is a popular shopping destination, home to multi-national businesses, and an important centre for arts and culture. In 2012 it became a UNESCO City of Literature in recognition of its literary heritage and its current contribution to publishing.

Of course the city is also associated with that icon of modern culture, Alan Partridge, the fictional co-creation of comedians Steve Coogan and Armando Iannucci, whose acclaimed television series and film "Alpha Papa" led to the introduction of a walking tour of the city based on the character's adventures.

There's plenty for sports enthusiasts, too. Football fans in the area might follow the popular club, Norwich City, affectionately known as the "Canaries". The team acquired its nickname from the city's history as home to Flemish textile workers who had fled persecution in 16th-century Spain. Finding a refuge in East Anglia, the new residents brought with them not only their skills in textiles, but also their pet canaries, which they began to breed. The popularity of the little birds led them to become associated with the city. ■

The Furry Dance

by Pamela Kavanagh.

ELSTON folks would have it that Furry Day, celebrated every May without fail in the town, was supposedly Flora Day, after the garlands worn at the event. Lowena had her own thoughts on the matter.

Widow Tallack at the end cottage had told her – confidentially, of course – that the name had the ring of old Cornish about it, and "furry" in the mother tongue came from *feur*, meaning fair or festival.

"Tes true, m'dear. But there, things were different then."

"How so?" Lowena wanted to know more.

"Well, now . . ." Widow Tallack's wrinkled brown face broke into a knowing smile. "That'd be telling, wouldn't it?"

Lowena had come away with her mind racing. Festival smacked of revelry and merriment, of feasting and time-honoured entertainment – minstrels, jugglers and maybe a fire-eater with his nail-bitingly perilous appetite for swallowing flames. There was an air of mystery about ancient custom. A thread of magic perhaps, touching fingertips down the years.

It was all a welcome break from the daily round, and to Lowena's reasoning a good deal more acceptable than today's way of doing things, dancing through the streets in white muslin and flowers in your hair, over cobblestones that hurt your feet something cruel. The flowers made her want to sneeze and wilted before the day was out, giving off a rank whiff of rotting grass.

"Frowning?" Mam, on her knees adjusting the hem of Lowena's new muslin, spoke through a mouthful of pins. "Mind the wind doan blow, our Lowena, and fix that face for good. Who will look twice at you then?"

Boys, Mam meant. Lowena tossed her head of dark brown curls. Time enough for boys. She wanted to live a bit first.

Mam secured the final pin and sat back on her heels, scrutinising the effect.

"Turn round for me. Slowly, now. Yes, that should do it. A sash this time, I think, with flowers in your hair."

Illustration by Martin Baines.

She went on to lament the fact that the man who did the programmes for Furry Day had let them down at the last minute and since no-one else could be found to fill the breach, how would folks know when everything was to take place?

Lowena did her best to sympathise, but could not in her heart rustle up much enthusiasm for the coming event. Even the singing of the traditional "Hal an Tow" song and the ritualistic plays performed at intervals in the streets had lost their appeal.

She wanted something different. She wanted festival. She wanted some excitement.

JAGO TALLACK put aside the wad of paper with the strictly ruled double lines and careful lettering, and delved into his leather satchel for the hard-backed sketchbook he had brought, the thick, yet unused vellum pages slightly yellowed with the years.

Below him in the valley, spring sunshine glinted on the rooftops and winding streets of the little town, bringing out the beauty of weathered stone and illuminating the tiny figures going about their work.

Jago knew he should really be practising the handwriting his boss demanded of him, but the urge at least to try to get the picture down, like his grandfather had done before him, was overwhelming. With luck he might even be able to capture the vibrancy and colour of the scene when he got back to Gran Tallack's with the set of watercolours she had given him, along with the sketchbook, that had belonged to his grandfather.

"See if you got his gift, boy. Your da never had it. But there, us is all different and talent can come in different ways." Gran Tallack's words chimed in his head.

Scents of wild thyme and gorse winnowed up from the grassy slope where he sat. Above, a flock of gulls wheeled and called, tempted inland by the freshly turned loam of an ox team and plough. It was very different from the stannary works on Coinagehall Street where the locally mined tin was checked for purity, and where he was serving his apprenticeship.

He put pencil to paper, but try as he might the hand that could form passably neat figures and letters refused to record what his eyes saw with such clarity. He was frowning over the page when a light step on the path made him glance up. A girl was approaching.

Emotion caught at Jago's throat. She was lovely – a typical Cornish girl with a mane of dark curls and firm rosy-brown cheeks.

She came confidently up and pulled to a stop beside him.

"Morning." She smiled, her merry eyes filling with curiosity. "I've not seen you before. Stranger to these parts, are you?"

"Not for much longer. I'm Jago Tallack."

"Tallack? Now I have it. You're Widow Tallack's lad's lad, come to stay while you're learning to be an accountant at the stannary."

"That's it. Word's got around, then."

"Oh, yes. It'll be nice for your gran, having a bit of company,"

Lowena said.

"I don't know about that. This is my afternoon off. She was mighty quick to shoo me out from under her feet."

"Oh, I expect she had her reasons. What's that you're doing? Drawing? We get quite a few artists here come summer."

Jago covertly shut the sketchbook on the picture he felt a child of five might have done better. Not for anything did he want this girl to see his attempt.

"Same where I'm from," he said. "Folks setting up easels along the quayside."

Lowena was interested.

"Oh? Where would that be?"

"Penberth Cove. It's a small place, nothing much there apart from the fishing. My da's got his own fleet. My brothers are both fishermen, but it's not for me. Figuring seems more my line. I was lucky to get taken on at the stannary, I reckon."

"Don't you like it?"

He shrugged.

"I like it well enough, but . . . oh, I don't know. I get a feeling there's more to life than slaving in a dusty office day in and day out."

A little breeze frisked, snatching at the sheets of papers and carrying some away.

Jago made to retrieve them but the girl was quicker and soon gathered them up.

"There. Are these more drawings? Oh!" She looked in puzzlement at the rows of lettering. "Not drawings, then."

"No." Jago relieved her of the papers. "It's for work. My boss insists on a mighty high standard of joined handwriting before an apprentice is allowed to record in the ledgers. We only learned printed capitals at the school."

"Me, too." She flopped down beside him, long skirts gathered around her, hands hugging her knees. "Show me some proper writing. Do my name. Go on. It's Lowena Carew."

HER smile was impossible to resist. Jago picked up his pencil and wrote the name in a commendable copperplate, ending with a flourish that might have satisfied even the most exacting boss.

"Oh!" Lowena gazed at the writing in open admiration. "That's beautiful, Jago. Your drawing must be really good."

"Well . . ." Honesty got the better of Jago. With a rueful quirk of his lips he picked up the sketchbook and showed her his sorry attempt. Lowena looked at him, sudden provocative amusement dancing in her eyes.

"Not exactly an artist, then."

Jago shook his head.

"No. Gran thought I might be like my grandfather, but I could have told her it was hopeless. This was his book. His paintings are on the walls."

"I know. I've seen them. They're really good, aren't they? So lively and fresh. Would you mind if I had a try? I liked drawing when I was at school, but there's no chance to do any these days."

IN silence he handed her the sketchbook and pencil. Lowena studied the subject for a moment or two, then positioned her hand. A few deft strokes and the scene below took shape before Jago's astonished gaze.

"Sakes! That's good. Try something else. A flower, or a bird. Try one of those seagulls over there."

She turned to a new page and sketched both, becoming more confident, the lines bolder and more detailed.

"There."

"Seems you have talent, Lowena. This bird could almost fly right off the paper."

She blushed beguilingly. Jago thought her the prettiest thing he had ever seen. No, it went deeper than that. She had something about her – a sense of purpose that was to be admired. Her bright chatter was refreshing after the sombre atmosphere of his workplace. He wondered how old she was. Younger than him, certainly. Sixteen, maybe. At nearly twenty he could almost be considered a man of the world.

Lowena had returned to gazing at her written name.

"Drawing is one thing, but handwriting is something else. I doubt I could ever write like this. Not even if I lived to be a hundred years old." She paused, and then said breathlessly, "Jago, I've just had a thought. It's Furry Day soon. Mam's sorting out my dress." She pulled a little face. "White muslin again! You do know about Furry Day, don't you? How the girls get dressed up in white frocks and garlands and dance through the streets? Children first, then the older ones. There's proper dancing for the grown-ups in the evening."

"Furry Day." He gave her a smile. "Gran did mention it. She spoke of a pageant and plays."

"Is that all? Didn't she say anything about how Furry Day used to be?"

"Old ways, you mean? Revels and such?"

"Yes. It all seemed such fun. Nothing like how it is today," Lowena told him.

"It's the way it has evolved. Some fairs are still as they always were. Penzance is."

"I'd love to see it. I'd love to go to a proper fair and be part of it. You get the feeling there's more behind it all than just flowers. Widow Tallack implied as much."

Jago shook his head.

"You mustn't heed any of that. Gran gets these notions."

Lowena's mouth set in a stubborn line.

"Well, I think she's right. What about the 'Hal an Tow' song on Furry Day? It's so ancient that no-one knows its meaning."

"Maybe just as well. What was this idea you had?"

"What?" Lowena frowned, then smiled. "Oh, yes. My mam said the man who does the programmes for Furry Day can't do it this time. The song goes on it, so visitors can join in the chorus, along with other things, like the times the dancing takes place and when the plays are performed."

"Well?" Jago looked puzzled.

"Don't you see?" Lowena went on eagerly. "We could design the programme between us. You could write out the details in your special script and I'll have a go at a decorative border and a picture for the cover. I think I can do it! The printers in town will print them out for us. They've got the very latest printing press."

He stared at her, his interest engaged.

"How long is there until Furry Day?"

"It's on the eighth of May. That's two whole weeks. Oh, come on, Jago!"

He smiled at her excitement.

"'Twill be good lettering experience . . ." He hesitated, and then pressed his paintbox and sketchbook into her hands. "You'd best have these for now. You may need to try out some ideas, my maid."

She blushed again, and clutched the items to her as if she had been given the world.

LOWENA went home in a daze. My maid, had been his words. No-one had ever called her that before, and it had done funny things to her heartbeat. She recalled Jago's warm brown eyes filled with admiration and wondered why at that very moment everything had suddenly felt at if it were sprinkled with golden dust. In the next breath she was wishing she could wear something more grown up on Furry Day. Green and white flock maybe, with pale green ribbons for her hair and a lace trim on her petticoat, like their Tegen had worn before she'd flown the nest to wed her Tomas.

She was still thinking about it all when she went up to bed that night. She wondered if Jago had made a start on the programme. How professional it would look in his distinctive script. Meanwhile, she would plan the border and cover picture.

On her chest of drawers lay the sketchbook. Oh, joy! Drawing lessons had been the high spot of her school days and there had been times when she remembered them with longing – the scratch-scratch of chalk on slate, the progression to real paper, the thrill of seeing a picture emerge . . .

Perhaps, she thought, a thread of magic had been weaving for her when she had come across Jago Tallack that morning. Furry Day magic? Widow Tallack had hinted as much. She then recalled Jago's laughing dismissal of his gran's beliefs, and shook her head sadly. That was boys for you. No imagination at all. Jago Tallack, for all his winning ways, was no different from the rest.

The realisation brought her down to earth with a thud.

✳   ✳   ✳   ✳

Working by the light of a taper after she had gone up to bed at night, Lowena tried out whatever idea sprang to mind. Page after page of the book became filled with drawings. Once she had a selection, she took the sketchbook along to Widow Tallack's cottage and together she and Jago set about designing the programme. It was cosy, sitting side by side at the table in the little house, the soft spring twilight pressing against the window, the fire crackling in the grate and the busy whirring of Widow Tallack's spinning wheel background to their young voices. Voices mostly in agreement, occasionally raised in lively argument.

"You can't put that!"

"Of course I can, Jago. See, it ties in with this. And this . . ."

Any clash of opinion usually ended in laughter, while the fire spat on in the grate and the spinning wheel continued its rhythmic song. Widow Tallack's face was in shadow but always that secretive little smile would be on her lips.

Life had never been so good for Lowena.

BY the start of the next week the design was done. Lowena showed the copy to her parents.

"What's this we got round the border, Lowena, lass?" Da said. "Cornish piskies?"

"That's right. The others are water sprites. Furry Day goes back a long way. People believed in those things back then."

The front cover drawing showed a winding procession of entertainers, including minstrels, a dance troupe in gaudy yellow and scarlet, a fortune teller with embroidered skirts and blouse, and so on.

Mixing paint, applying it to the page with the fine-tipped squirrel-hair brush provided, Lowena had been lost in a world all her own. She could think of no better way of spending her time. But now the unwelcome truth was dawning. Soon she would have to give both paints and book back to the owner and life would shrink back to the lack-lustre round of helping Mam about the house. No scrambling to light the taper and pick up her paintbrush when a sudden idea woke her in the night. No evening trips to the end cottage and Jago, their two heads bent closely together as they poured over their work while Widow Tallack sat spinning by the fire.

Da was still contemplating the programme copy and Lowena's heart gave an anxious little bump.

"Is it good enough?" she asked him.

"Good enough?" He gave a small laugh of disbelief. "I'll say it is. Tes better than any we's had before. I shall be dropping this off at the printers tomorrow on my way to work. Seems you's gifted, my girl. And to think we never knew. You can tell that grandson of Widow Tallack him's got a mighty fine hand with a pen an' all. All credit to the pair of you." His look went to Mam. "Doan you agree, wife?"

Mam just sniffed.

"Tes well enough. Just doan you forget there's more important things, Lowena. Our Tegen didn't get her Tomas by squinting night after night over a candlelit page. Girls need their beauty sleep, mind me?"

Lowena sighed inwardly. Really, there was no pleasing some folks.

Furry Day came in with blown May blossom and blue skies. Townsfolk and visitors alike – the latter having been streaming since daybreak into Helston on foot, in pony-trap and on farm-cart – lined the streets to watch the show. Nodding smiles went to the children who danced their best, flowers bobbing, and during a later procession, depending on age and gender, expressions were wistful or appreciative as the troupe of white-clad girls tripped by.

Plays were applauded, the pageant exclaimed over, the "Hal an Tow" heartily sung.

Best of all for two members of the gathering was the praise for the new-style programme of events.

"A worthy keepsake of the day," was heard more than once.

"Proper little artist, your Lowena." This was to Mam, who nodded and simpered, while Da looked on proudly.

Words such as tasteful, interesting, and even stunning, were tossed about. Helston, it seemed, was impressed by the shift from the normal.

EVENING came and couples drifted in for the adult dancing. Jago sought Lowena out. His face was eager. He took her hand.

"Seems you'd best keep those painting tools, my maid. We've just had a request for a programme for the Helston Harvest Fair in September. There's been another for the Knill Ceremony in July. That's at St Ives. Word about us looks to be spreading. Are you interested?"

"Yes! Oh, yes," Lowena said breathlessly.

Jago's lean, handsome face grew serious.

"You know, we two work well together. There's more we could consider. Lowena, have you ever thought of designing a greetings card? Christmas, Eastertide, birthdays and such."

"Well, no, I can't say I have . . . but I could do it. I know I could!"

"You do the illustration while I scribe the lettering. There's a growing demand for cards. I heard that in London folks pay quite a bit for a decent one, and ours would be the best money could buy." He stopped, and then said a little bashfully, "Sometimes a line or two of verse comes to me. I reckon I could write the verses for the cards."

"Oh, could you?" Admiration throbbed in Lowena's voice. "We could get them printed here in town and sell them locally. It could even lead to greater things."

"Exactly," Jago said. "My da's fishing fleet started with one boat and just him to sail her. And look at it now. Six fishing smacks and he's taking on another. Anything can grow if you go about it sensibly."

"But what about your job at the stannary?" Lowena asked. "Your apprenticeship?"

"What of it? I'll serve my time. Accountancy skills can come in useful when running a business." His eyes flashed in sudden excitement. "Think about it, Lowena. We'd start off in a small way. Keep the overheads down. No shop premises at first, as that would be a drain on finances. We could trade at those fairs you so wanted to see."

"Have a stall, you mean?" She clapped her hands in delight. "Oh, yes!"

At that moment the band struck up, the sound lifting to the starry evening. Jago took her hand.

"Dance with me?" he asked.

"What, in crumpled muslin and faded flowers?" Laughter rang in her voice.

"You'll be the prettiest here," Jago said, and swept her into the dance.

I'VE been thinking," Mam said a day or two later. "Being as you's branching out into the artist trade, we can forget white muslin in future. What about a nice flock next year?"

She added, as if in afterthought, "Him's a fine young man, is Jago Tallack."

Lowena remembered Jago's arms around her as they dipped and whirled unheeding over the lumpy cobblestones, Widow Tallack looking on, with the knowing eyes and secret smile. She knew a thing or two, did Widow Tallack.

Lowena gave Mam a nod.

"Yes, he is," she agreed.

"Seems this is a Furry Day to remember," Jago had whispered to her, before pressing an oh, so sweet kiss on her lips.

He could not have said a truer word! ■

I'd Like To Know...

Sit back and enjoy this classic selection of vintage queries from the lovely readers of the "Friend"!

Q **I LOVE** to have cut flowers at home, but some of my friends have very different views on how to keep them looking their best. One swears by a drop of lemonade, while another drops a penny in the vase and another puts an aspirin in tap water. Can you please tell me the best way to keep cut flowers looking good for longer?

– Mrs H.H., Boreham.

A **THE** little packet of plant food that comes with cut flowers from a florist contains bactericides that kill bacteria, yeasts and fungi. A copper penny is a fungicide and acts to preserve the water from too many yeasts and fungi. Aspirin is an acid and helps to kill bacteria growth. Or you could add two tablespoons of lemon juice or vinegar to two pints of water, as they are both acidic. Other guidelines on keeping cut flowers fresh are to place the freshly cut blooms in cold water, not hot, and to leave in the fridge for up to six hours before arranging them. Re-cut the stems every two days and change the water every day for the very best results.

. . . .

Q **I WOULD** be very interested to know what type of bean is used in tins of baked beans. Can you help?

– Mrs M.G., Banstead.

A **ALTHOUGH** they are called baked beans, most baked beans are actually stewed in a tomato-based sauce. And the beans most commonly used are haricot beans, sometimes called navy beans. Canned beans, often with pork, were among the very first convenience foods. Up until World War II, Heinz Baked Beans were produced with a piece of pork. This was, however, removed from the cans due to rationing and never reintroduced.

Illustration by Helen Welsh/Thinkstockphotos.

Making History

by Angela Lanyon.

DO you remember the war?" Mrs Bridges straightened up from her weeding and peered over the wall. There, staring at her, was Ellie-Jane from the top of the road, her eyes bright and inquisitive like a small bird.

"Well, yes, I do actually," she said, wondering what was coming next.

"I'm so sorry, Mrs Bridges."

Ellie-Jane's mum, Rita, was hurrying up the road in pursuit of her daughter. "I've told her not to bother you."

Although it had been some years since Jeff, her beloved husband of nearly 50 years, had passed over, people in the village still seemed to think she needed treating like a fragile piece of glass.

"It's all right," she told Rita. "I'm only doing a bit of gardening. It's such a nice day it seems a pity to waste it."

That was true. The previous week it had rained non-stop and she'd had to make an effort not to let the grey skies get her down.

"The weeds come out a treat when the soil's damp."

"It's to do with history. They're doing World War Two at school," Rita said. "It seems Year Six always does it."

"I don't understand all this 'year' business," Mrs Bridges said, dropping a handful of weeds into an old bucket and looking down at Ellie-Jane. "It was classes when I went to school."

"Will you tell me about it, please?" Ellie-Jane's hair was blowing around in the wind. "I'm supposed to find someone old and ask them questions."

"Ellie-Jane, you shouldn't say that," Rita broke in. "It's very rude."

Mrs Bridges laughed.

"Well, I am old! But what do you want to know?"

"We all have to find out about the war. Because it's a history project."

"She's supposed to find someone who was alive then and ask them questions about what they remember," Rita explained. "Tell her what it was like."

Mrs Bridges nodded.

"While there's still some of us around, I expect." She looked at Ellie-Jane. "Do you know how long ago it was?"

"It was nineteen-forty."

"And how old do you think that makes me?"

Ellie-Jane's face was screwed up in a effort to work it out.

"Don't worry, I'll tell you. As old as my tongue and a bit older than my teeth." Mrs Bridges laughed. "And that's saying something. Does it have to be this minute?" she went on, thinking about her dirty hands and the washing-up still sitting on the draining board. "Maybe your mum would bring you across one afternoon after school?"

Ellie-Jane smiled and her eyes sparkled.

"That would be a good idea. But I don't want her to be a bother," Rita said.

"Let's make it next Monday, shall we, Ellie-Jane?" Mrs Bridges smiled at the girl, who was nodding enthusiastically. "That'll give you the weekend to think of the questions you want to ask me. Oh, and don't forget to bring a notebook with you so you can write it all down."

And that would give me a chance to sort out all the things I want to remember, Mrs Bridges thought as she picked up the weed-filled bucket and went round to the back of the cottage.

T HE war. That was a long time ago! She squirted liquid soap on her hands and washed them under the tap. That was one of the things that had been short during the war – soap.

Not that her mum would ever have let her use it as an excuse for coming to the table with dirty hands.

"Backs as well as fronts," she'd say, and then make her turn them over to prove it.

Not that it had made much difference the day the bomb fell. She could remember sheltering under the big kitchen table and listening to the planes overhead, and then hearing a sort of swoosh and the bricks thumping down on to the top of their refuge.

Was that the sort of thing she should be telling young Ellie-Jane? Children, in her opinion, had a right to grow up without being afraid. But then, with all that was on the television, how could they? Maybe it was better that they knew things could go badly sometimes, so that they'd be on their guard and be prepared to do something about it.

Drying her hands, she went through into the sitting-room and pulled open the drawer where she kept all her photographs. What a muddle! Clearing out the drawer was something she'd been meaning to do for ages. Michelle and Sally, her two daughters, had been nagging her for goodness knew how long.

"If you don't write the names on the back of these, we shan't know who people are!" Sally had pulled out an old black-and-white photograph of two children on a beach and had pushed it under her mother's nose. "Now, who's that?"

Mrs Bridges had pulled on her glasses and stared at it.

"Well, I never!"

"So you do recognise them?"

"Of course I do. I'm not senile yet! It's me on the beach at Scarborough. Just before the war, it was."

Sally pointed to the child with the long dark hair.

"If this is you, who's the other one?"

"Hilary. I don't know her other name. They stayed at the same guesthouse. They were there every year."

"What happened to her?"

"Goodness me, I don't know. There was a war on, you know. Things were upside-down."

No, she thought, studying the picture, they'd never gone back to Scarborough again. After the war broke out there were a lot of things they never did again. But then, if there hadn't been a war she'd never have met Jeff.

She sat back in her chair and stared at the drawer. It was too heavy for her to lift out. Eight, she'd been then, and now she was well over eighty! As old as her tongue and quite a lot older than her teeth. At least she'd a nice set of comfortable dentures now. That was another thing that had improved.

Mrs Bridges shook her head impatiently. Her dad would have said she was wool-gathering. What was she supposed to be doing? Finding some photographs that she could show to Ellie-Jane.

She bent forward and started to lift out the wallets of photos. Before long she had them scattered all around her, but she still hadn't found what she was looking for.

ONE of their neighbours had taken a picture of their house, or the remains of it, anyway. A miracle, they'd called it. There had been a newspaper cutting of 17 Wisteria Avenue, not much more than a heap of bricks, and her mum covered with dirt after being pulled out from under the table. Mrs Bridges remembered that.

After the rumble of the bricks it was dark for what seemed like a very long time. Then there were voices and her mum called out. After that there was a bit of daylight, then someone called again and then her mum was being hauled out

Thank You For Colours

THANK YOU, Lord, for the colours of the world,
The beauty of the world for us to share,
The wonder of the planets, moon and stars
And all the joy of nature everywhere.
Thank you, Lord, for the colours of my life,
For shining rainbows after times of storm,
For quiet moments when the world is still
And memories return to keep me warm.

Thank you, Lord, for the colours of my mind –
You take away the grey when I'm depressed,
You show me healing blue and gentle green,
Reminding me that I am truly blessed.
The blue of sky, the mauve of evening clouds,
The silver frost, the blossom trees in May,
The many precious gifts that I can see.
Lord, thank you for these colours every day.

– Iris Hesselden.

and all she could see were her mum's feet disappearing. Her skirt would be torn, she'd thought, and Mum would be showing her knickers. And then it was her turn and she was sneezing and coughing, and someone was wrapping her in a blanket and telling her she was a brave little girl.

She hadn't wanted to be called a little girl – after all, she'd just turned ten. But that was her first meeting with Jeff. He was a boy from up the road who was waiting to go into the RAF, and who came back six years later to see if she was all right.

"You hardly know him," her mum said. "Anyway, he's a lot older than you."

"Only seven years," she countered. "Look at Princess Elizabeth. Prince Philip's a lot older than her."

"That's as maybe," her dad said, "but you're only sixteen. You hang on at school a bit longer and get your leaving certificate, then you can think about getting wed."

* * * *

If it was all right for royalty, it was all right for her. And so it had proved. But they'd had to wait. Jeff was a qualified electrician when he left the RAF and she was a State Registered Nurse, and together they'd shared nearly 50 happy years. Since that first day, when he'd stretched out his hand through the dust and darkness and had pulled her into the light, he'd always been there for her.

The cutting was in an envelope and she took it out and smoothed it across her lap. Faded and torn at the edges it might be, but it still had the power to make her heart pound and bring tears to her eyes. Perhaps she'd not show it to Ellie-Jane. It wouldn't do for the little girl to see her in tears. But then again . . . Maybe she'd sleep on it. After all, there was the whole weekend before she had to make a decision.

Monday came, and she was no nearer making up her mind about what to do. It wasn't like her to dither; she'd always been one for coming to a decision quickly. "Rushing things", her dad used to say. She found she was recalling a lot of things he used to say. Looking at that cutting hadn't half brought back the past! All the stories her dad used to tell her about when he'd been a lad, and now she was going to be doing the same.

History, that was what Ellie-Jane and her mum had called it. But it wasn't history, not to Mrs Bridges's way of thinking. History was kings and queens and knights on horseback, not getting pulled out of bombed buildings.

"Henry V" – she'd been taken to see that when she was in the top class, she remembered that. The numbers on the English side hadn't been great. One thought led to another and she was thinking about the Few. All those brave airmen! And then, for no reason at all, Little Red Riding Hood popped into her head. She laughed. Of course! She'd been wearing her red dressing-gown when she was pulled out of the ruins.

Well, Red Riding Hood had had a happy ending. The woodcutter had slit open the wolf's stomach and out had popped Granny, right as rain. Mrs Bridges imagined Granny must have been just as startled and relieved to be pulled out of the wolf's tummy as she and her mum had been when they emerged into the daylight.

That was a story. But this was her story, her adventure. And she decided she would tell Ellie-Jane. The tale of Little Red Riding Hood didn't say what happened to Granny after the wolf was killed. Maybe she wasn't a very elderly granny and married the woodcutter, or maybe Red Riding Hood married the woodcutter. Mrs Bridges turned to look at the photograph of her beloved Jeff. Not one of the Few, but one of the many who kept the planes in the air.

She looked down at her wrinkled, work-worn hand. The hand that, all those years ago, she'd stretched out, to feel his firm, warm grip tighten and pull her free of all the dust and dirt.

Yes, she would tell Ellie-Jane and show her the cutting, and assure her that adventures and disasters didn't have to end in tears.

I'm part of history, she thought as she began arranging biscuits on a plate and putting out orange juice for Ellie-Jane and mugs for herself and Rita. It's not just kings and queens, it's people like me and Jeff, and Ellie-Jane, perhaps, one day.

We are the ones who make history. ▓

Eildon Hills, Scottish Borders

RISING over the historic town of Melrose, the Eildon Hills offer walkers rewarding views over the Borders. The remnants of ancient volcanoes, the three peaks dominate the surrounding landscape, though local folklore has another explanation, as the rock was said to have been "cleft in three" by the mediaeval scholar and mathematician Michael Scot, who was reputed to be a wizard.

Archaeologists have found that the area was occupied in prehistoric times. They have discovered ancient burial mounds and an Iron Age hill fort as well as the remains of more than 300 hut platforms that would once have supported wooden roundhouses, suggesting that this was once quite a busy settlement, housing up to 2,000 people.

Later, the invading Roman army found the commanding position on the hills useful as the base for a signal tower to enable them to send messages over long distances.

Today, the peaceful site is popular as a destination for walkers and nature lovers, keen to spot the abundant bird- and wildlife in the area. ■

73

A Part To Play

by Patricia Clark.

GWEN got up from her desk and grabbed her coat.

"Doubt is resolved by action alone," she muttered. This was her favourite quotation to galvanise her when, staring at her typewriter, the words refused to come. Not that she could remember who wrote it, but it had served her well in these difficult weeks.

First, the man she had thought of as the love of her life had ended their relationship, then the London Women's Institute offices, where she worked on the organisation's magazine "Town And Country", had been bombed. Finally, her flat had taken a hit. So, while all the office equipment was being moved to the new premises in Puddephat's Farm, Hertfordshire, she had decamped to the Sussex cottage left to her by an unmarried aunt.

Yes, she certainly was one of the lucky ones. She had somewhere pleasant to live which was safer than the city. Also, she could work on her articles here.

But she was finding it hard to settle, and her brief meeting with Gareth, the village schoolmaster, when she was moving in hadn't helped. His exuberance and zest for life was uncomfortably similar to the man she still thought of fondly in her quiet moments.

Perhaps exercise and a breath of fresh air would help to clear her mind and steady her emotions. Her piece had to be written by the end of the week and so far she had only managed a few general remarks on growing vegetables to help the war effort. Yes, a visit to the village allotments would surely inspire her to write something the WI readers would find interesting.

Almost hidden away at the other end of the village, the allotments occupied a spot beyond the church and the school. Several men were working on theirs as she walked by, then one cheery pensioner with a kind face smiled and doffed his cap.

"I'm Ben," he said. "If you want an allotment there are a few spare."

Another man, a few yards away, briefly looked up from his weeding.

"Don't be daft. She's from the big city. Wouldn't want to get her hands dirty."

"I'm Gwen." She turned to address both men. "Bombed out of my flat and office in London."

Ben warmly shook her hand.

"Pleased to meet you. We're a friendly bunch. Even this old grouch!"

This spurred the grumpy man to shake her hand.

Illustration by David Young.

"I'll show you around." Ben stuck his spade in the soil.

"That would be good," Gwen said, "but I'm not wanting an allotment."

As they walked she told him about her work on the magazine and Lord Woolton's "Dig For Victory" campaign, which she was writing about.

"Not that you people need much encouraging." She stopped to admire a particularly immaculate plot.

"I think these celery plants need banking up again," Ben remarked. "Young Gareth, the schoolmaster, will be on it any day. His father's a farmer in the Lincolnshire Fens. The celery king, they call him. He supplies all the big stores in London."

Gwen nodded politely. She didn't want to hear any more about Gareth and his family, but Ben persisted.

"He wanted Gareth to come in with him, but he was dead set on doing his bit for the war by enlisting." He shook his head. "He failed the medical – a heart murmur, I think he said – and chose schoolteaching as the best alternative."

"I wonder he has time for an allotment," Gwen said, walking on. "I would really like to see some plots that are not used, or which just need more care and attention to increase production."

"Of course." Ben smiled. "You've work to do."

"Sorry," she said. "I didn't mean to be so abrupt." She really shouldn't take out her stupid prejudices against a young man she barely knew on this friendly man.

"Don't worry." He kicked a stone off the grass path. "I like a woman with spirit. Had we been blessed with a daughter, I would have liked her to have a mind of her own. It's the thing nowadays. This war's brought it about."

Surely women had always had minds of their own, Gwen thought, as another allotment caught her attention, carefully dug and weeded but with no plants at all.

THAT belongs to the owner of the village store, a newcomer," Ben explained. "He's got plans for growing all sorts of fancy stuff but hasn't got round to it yet."

"A shame," Gwen said, noting the position of the allotment in the little notebook she had been filling with notes as they talked.

She pointed to another one next to it. What must once have been a flourishing strawberry crop was now reduced to a tangle of runners barely visible beneath a carpet of weeds.

"An elderly couple owned this," Ben explained, "and tended it tirelessly until the husband died quite suddenly. Now his wife has neither the will nor the energy to do much to it."

"It would take a mammoth amount of organisation and sheer hard work to put these right." Depressed, Gwen looked down her list.

"Well, I must be off," Ben said brightly. "Look, it's break-time." He pointed to the schoolyard filling up with noisy children. "And there's Gareth on duty. If you're quick you could catch a word with him. See what help he can muster from the children if you want to make a difference."

He waved to attract Gareth's attention and then was gone, leaving Gwen with no option but to renew her brief acquaintance with this man she was so wary of.

He was sorting out two quarrelsome pupils; the girl complaining the boy kept pulling the ribbons off her plaits, the boy insisting she provoked him by trying to trip him up.

"I can see you're busy," Gwen said quickly. "I'll catch you some other time."

"No, wait, please." Gareth gave her a welcoming smile and then altered his expression as he turned back to the children and gave them a few firm words. "You two. Go inside and stand by my desk, and no fighting.

"They'll be friends by the time I get there." He laughed. "Now, tell me what I can do for you."

"I write for a magazine and am concentrating on the 'Dig For Victory' initiative, starting with allotments. I have . . ."

". . . already had a guided tour of ours by Ben," he finished. "I guess he suggested I could provide some more info."

"Well, yes," she replied, "if you can."

He looked at his watch.

"I must blow the whistle and get the children back to work. I'll call round this evening, if that's all right with you." There was that pleasant smile again!

"Of course. Thank you." What else could she say? Why shouldn't the local schoolmaster want to help a newcomer to the village? She must forget that he was naturally charming and attractive.

After all, she needed all the help she could muster.

B Y the time Gareth arrived Gwen had rewritten her allotment notes and added some suggestions that came to mind. He read through them carefully.

"Seems to me that you are not just interested in writing a piece for the magazine, but want to do something with the wasted plots here." He leaned forward, elbows on the table, his brown eyes wide with his infectious enthusiasm. "But who are you going to persuade to do the work?"

"That's where you come in," she went on quickly. "You are teacher to a number of energetic children. A ready-made band of land workers!"

"Maybe." He thought for a moment. "But I'll need some help." He leaned back in the chair and looked at her. "Someone with connections to the worthy Women's Institute," he teased, "and, as we haven't a branch in this village, perhaps . . ."

It was so easy to say yes, Gwen thought after Gareth had left and she sat down at her desk. And yes, she really would enjoy taking part in this important campaign.

She read the notes she had made when they talked, identifying then dividing up the necessary tasks. Gwen would visit villagers who had problems tending their allotments and assure them that help was at hand, while Gareth would contact the parents of the pupils in his top class and hope for some limited help from sensible pupils and the other two teachers as well.

My article, she typed, *is not from the dugout, as the Editor's piece last month was, as in order to escape from the constant air battles going on above us, we are on the move to new quarters. I am temporarily in a small village, and am involved in plans the residents are making to support the Government's "Dig For Victory" campaign. I will bring you news every month and hope it may encourage you to have a go! First . . .*

She tapped away, the only sound in the cottage; outside, there was just the occasional hoot of an owl. A positive plan made her feel so much better, and then there was Gareth – no longer a threat to her peace of mind, but simply an ally in an essential cause.

CONTACTING the allotment owners proved easier than Gwen anticipated, thanks to her decision to lead by example by digging up most of her front lawn to grow vegetables.

She had only been at work for an hour when a delicate but lively-looking lady, who turned out to be Kathryn, the widow with the neglected strawberry patch, came over and introduced herself.

"I hope I'm not interrupting you," she said, " but I saw you in the allotments and I felt quite ashamed about mine. I don't know what my late husband would say if he saw it in such a mess. It was his pride and joy. I wonder if you could give me some help."

Gwen smiled.

"I'm glad of an excuse to put down my spade for a while. There's a lot of work needed on many plots, I'm afraid."

Kathryn nodded, looking quite downcast as Gwen went on.

"Help is at hand for people like you who are struggling, yet want to make a difference to the amount of food our country can grow," she reassured her and outlined the plan she and Gareth had devised.

"I'm not sure about the children." Kathryn frowned. "They will need supervision."

"That's where Gareth and some parents will come in."

"I see. Our young schoolmaster has it all organised," Kathryn said. "That's all right, then." But her tone and straight face suggested she felt differently. "I can't help thinking that if my nephew hadn't joined up, he would be the one teaching here, and safe. Gareth was his replacement."

"Yes, I know," Gwen replied quietly. It was understandable that Kathryn felt bitter.

* * * *

Gwen couldn't believe how easily their plans had been accepted. She had persuaded the village shopkeeper that to tend his allotment would not only look better for the villagers, but his idea of growing asparagus could be very profitable. With her suggestion that he might try any other slightly unusual vegetables, he was firmly on side.

Kathryn, meanwhile, had approached the older people on the list and received a universal yes to the proposed offers of help, and Gareth was a regular visitor at Gwen's cottage, keeping her up to date with developments while enjoying a working supper together.

It was Friday evening, the eve of the launch, when all the helpers and anyone else who cared to come were to gather at the allotments ready to start work.

After The Holiday

THE holiday's over – I'm rested and tanned,
It's all left behind me: the sea and the sand.
And though I've fine trinkets and gifts to unpack,
I feel rather woebegone now that I'm back!
How quickly, it seems, I fall into routine –
I've almost forgotten the places I've been.
I've left a hotel so delightfully posh,
Now I'm home with this big pile of clothing to wash!
Then I must shop, so we've dinner for later
(Not *à la carte*, sadly, or served by the waiter).
Oh, this time last week, I traversed distant shores –
It's now back to cleaning and other dull chores.
But, never mind, while I get all of this done,
I'll dream of vacations – and plan the next one!

– Emma Canning.

As usual, Gareth helped Gwen clear away the plates from tonight's supper – "Wartime Stew" made from a WI recipe.

"Very little meat and loads of dumplings but still tasty," was Gareth's verdict.

"Flatterer." She laughed, feeling relaxed in his company. A true friendship had developed between them and she was enjoying it.

With numerous pieces of paper spread out on the table detailing their plans, Gareth was keen to draw all this information together.

"The parents are very willing to help, but I think it's important to get as many children involved as we can."

"Start them off with simple tasks," Gwen responded.

"Useful but fun," Gareth insisted and soon they were bouncing ideas off each other as before.

"Start with tidying small patches first. Even the rough bits that border the allotment, I think."

"Which would be a great challenge for some of the energetic boys," Gareth finished. "They have plenty of surplus energy to burn."

At last they came to a halt. Gwen picked up her pencil to scribble down their ideas.

Gareth laughed.

"I know you are a writer of articles," he said, "but there's no need to put everything on paper. It's a precious commodity nowadays."

"I know. But you are just as wasteful," she retaliated, stretching across him to point at all the pages of notes he'd brought.

Inadvertently brushing his hand, she jumped, and just about managed to subdue the redness she could feel creeping on to her face. Romance certainly wasn't on her agenda, and probably not on his.

"It feels good doing something practical for the war, doesn't it?" she said quickly to hide her momentary lapse. "Even if we are on the sidelines."

"Some people would say we are not in the same league as those who are fighting," Gareth replied thoughtfully, and she guessed he meant Kathryn.

"Maybe." Gwen changed the subject. "Talking to you makes me realise how much I miss the comradeship of the office, working and socialising with like-minded people."

"Have you anyone special in London?" he asked as if he had read her mind.

Her "No" sounded unconvincing, so she added briefly, "There was once. Not any more."

F RIDAY night was a disturbed one for most villagers, with enemy planes flying from nine o'clock onwards.

Poor Londoners, Gwen thought as she struggled to fall asleep, keen to wake up early and get on with the job.

It was a glorious autumn morning, the allotments bathed in mellow sunshine flattering even those overgrown with weeds and adding to the effect of a pleasing patchwork of colours.

Gareth and the two other teachers distributed the tools with strict instructions to the children.

"Remember, Jimmy Botting, a spade has a sharp edge."

"I know, sir. You told us yesterday." He grinned cheekily, pushing back his fringe and leaving a smear on his face from fingers already grimy with dirt. "It's for digging. Not fighting."

Gwen recognised him as the boy she had seen in the playground annoying the girl with plaits on the day that this enterprise began. It seemed such a long time ago, but it was only a few days. So much had happened since then.

"Perhaps you would like to help Ben organise these rascals," Gareth suggested to the lad and Gwen readily agreed.

"He's only digging the easy stuff," Jimmy quipped, thrusting his spade vigorously through a tangle of tree roots.

"Look how much we've done already," another grimy lad chipped in. "We could grow some potatoes in this."

"Or wheat," another put in.

Gareth raised his eyebrows and wandered off.

"Don't be daft," Jimmy scoffed. "Farmers do that."

The banter continued as they all got on with the work. Ben and Gwen were enjoying it as much as the boys, and they were making real inroads when the drone of a single aeroplane shattered the peace.

Everyone stopped work and looked up as the German plane drew nearer.

"It's all right," someone shouted. "It's coming from London, on its way back home. Look! There's a Spitfire after him."

Jimmy and his mates stood stock still, fascinated as if a dogfight between two planes was just a spectacle.

"Into the playground," Gareth shouted. "Get behind the back wall. That plane could still have bombs on board. It could crash with them if shot down."

"The British pilot will try to disable him, then chase him out towards the sea," Ben explained to the anxious parents, though he knew it wasn't always possible to be so precise.

Gathered inside the playground, Gareth and Gwen did a quick head count of the assembled children.

"There should be more," he said to Gwen.

Both scanned the allotments but Gwen spotted him first.

"There! Under the trees where I was working, someone's moving. Oh, no!" she cried.

"Jimmy!" Gareth shouted, recognising him at once. "Stay where you are!"

"Look at him," the boy's mates muttered. "He's daft. And he can't hear you."

There Jimmy was, racing back and forth in and out of the trees, arms outstretched and making aeroplane noises.

GARETH was off in a second. He grabbed Jimmy and pulled him under the trees.

The group, spectators at a real life-and-death drama, held their breath. Gwen went cold while up above the dogfight between the two planes intensified. Again and again the Spitfire's guns hit the bomber, which finally disappeared out of sight behind the trees and crashed, they learned later, on the downs before reaching the Channel.

Gwen was still shivering when Gareth and Jimmy returned, to a rousing cheer of relief.

"So much for teaching being a safe occupation." Kathryn put her arm round Gwen and helped pour out those much-needed cups of tea. "Our young schoolteacher is a good man and brave," she went on. "I've been narrow-minded and bigoted, thinking it's only the men who fight who are heroes. We all have our part to play, young and old, in any way we can. I see that now."

Gwen smiled and thought that Kathryn wasn't the only one to have learned from this exercise. It had also helped her to put the past behind her. She was glad to have Gareth as a friend and, judging by the way she'd felt when he was selflessly putting himself in danger, perhaps more than a friend one day. ∎

I'd Like To Know...

Sit back and enjoy this classic selection of vintage queries from the lovely readers of the "Friend"!

Q **MY** husband loves the "Carry On" films and wondered how many of them were made. Could you also please tell us the names of the actors who starred in them?

– Mrs T.R., Brighton.

A **THE** "Carry On" films were a long-running series of low-budget British comedies. There were 29 original films and one compilation made between 1958 and 1978 at Pinewood Studios. One final film was made in 1992. Kenneth Williams starred in 26 of the films, Joan Sims in 24, Charles Hawtrey in 23, Sid James in 19, Hattie Jacques in 14 and Barbara Windsor in 10.

Q **MY** friend told me that digestive biscuits got their name because they were believed to be medicinal when they were first sold. I can't believe this is true and wondered if you could settle the argument.

– Mrs I.P., Melton Mowbray.

A **DIGESTIVES** biscuits go all the way back to 1876 when they were manufactured by Huntley & Palmers. They are a sweetmeal biscuit and traditionally contain coarse brown wheat flour, sugar, vegetable oil, wholemeal, raising agents (usually sodium bicarbonate) and salt. The biscuits were given the name "digestive" because it was believed that the sodium bicarbonate in them could act as an antacid. However, the tiny amount of sodium bicarbonate in each biscuit made this very unlikely.

Q **COULD** you please let me know the meaning of the following phrase that appears on all British passports – *Dieu et mon droit*?

– Mr J.E., County Tyrone.

A **THE** phrase refers to the divine right of the monarch to govern, and is said to have been first used as the royal motto of England by King Henry V in the 15th century. The motto is French and translates as "God and my right".

Illustration by Kirk Houston/Thinkstockphotos.

Count Your Blessings

by Susan Blackburn.

G ENE and Jackie Beamond awoke as usual to the sound of
Classic FM and the welcome hiss of the Teasmade.

"Good morning, darling." Jackie handed Gene his cup of tea.

"And a very good morning to you, my love," Gene replied.

"Bus pass renewal day today," Jackie reminded her husband.
"I've booked the car service for ten-thirty."

"That should give us plenty of time to get these old bones moving," Gene
said, kissing the end of Jackie's nose.

"Come in," she called in response to the tap on their bedroom door. "Good
morning, Sheila. What's the weather doing out there today?"

"At long last, the sun's shining!" Sheila replied.

"Of course it is. The sun always shines on the righteous," Gene quipped.

Sheila, their home care worker, grinned back at the two beaming faces and thought yet again how extremely lucky she was to be caring for these two amazing people. At seventy-five and seventy-three respectively, they were both crippled with arthritis, in constant pain and had to use walking frames. But she'd never heard them grumble in all the five years she'd worked for them. Whatever she felt like, after a little while in their company, Sheila found she was on top of the world and counting her blessings.

Sheila's husband, Stan, drove for the voluntary car service and arrived promptly to pick up Gene and Jackie. Showered and smartly dressed, they duly set off for their local council offices where the renewal of bus passes was taking place.

⋆　⋆　⋆　⋆

Rachel Meadows awoke as usual to the intrusive buzzing of the alarm clock. It had to be loud or she just slept right through it. Not that she would have cared. Burrowing under the duvet and going back to sleep was what she had wished for every morning since she and Ian had split up.

It wasn't even as if she loved her job, which was just a necessary means to an end. It meant she earned enough money for the mortgage on her tiny cottage, for food on the table and the running of her car.

Rachel showered, dressed and gulped down coffee and toast. Sighing deeply, she shrugged on her coat, banged the cottage door behind her and made her way to the car.

I am absolutely sure, she thought morosely, that this will be yet another joyless and frustrating day.

ERE we are." Stan pulled up in front of the council offices in one of the disabled bays.

Having been solicitously helped inside the teeming council offices and duly registered for their appointment, Gene and Jackie made their way to the crowded waiting-room.

"Oh, dear, there don't seem to be any seats left, Jackie," Gene remarked, doing a sweep of the room with his bright blue eyes.

Despite his stooped stance over his walking frame, Gene still had a presence whenever he entered a room. Ever optimistic, the glass always half full, he seemed confident somebody would offer him and his wife a seat.

And sure enough, a couple of lads in hoodies and low-slung jeans stood up.

"Here you are, Grandad," the taller of the two called over in well-spoken tones. "There's a couple of seats over here, look."

"Less of the grandad!" Gene joked. "But thanks, lads. Much obliged to you.

'Never judge a book by its cover' proved true yet again, my love," Gene murmured to Jackie as they gratefully sank down on the vacated seats.

They watched the proceedings in the hectic office with interest. They soon got into conversation with others awaiting their turn and, as always seemed the way with them, they made the people they chatted with feel as if life was just a little bit more worth living.

✳   ✳   ✳   ✳

"Mr and Mrs Beamond, eleven o'clock appointment, counter five, please."

Rachel looked across to where Gene and Jackie were making their slow progress towards her. She sighed. The morning had not gone well, the computer was playing up and she was running behind.

"Good morning, I'm sorry to have kept you waiting. Could I have your ID documentation, please?" she intoned on autopilot when at last the Beamonds were settled.

They both turned their full gaze on Rachel. The babble of people faded away and she suddenly felt as if they were the only people left in the world.

"We've been watching you. Rachel, isn't it?" Jackie asked softly, peering at Rachel's name badge. "You're a very unhappy young lady, aren't you?"

Rachel frowned. Who were these people? Giving a little sob, she blindly punched a few figures into the computer.

It crashed. It was the last straw. Tears streamed down Rachel's face.

"It must be time for your lunch break," Jackie said, pushing a tissue into Rachel's hand. "You get off, my dear. We can come back later for our bus passes when we've had something to eat, too. It's marvellous how we can get about on the buses now we can't drive any more, isn't it, Gene?" she went on with a smile. "And everyone is so kind and helpful. It's lovely, too, the way it gives us so many opportunities to chat to people."

Rachel found herself helping Jackie and Gene to the lift. Then she scurried off to repair her ravaged face before making her way to the café next door. She wasn't hungry but she desperately needed a break.

THE first people Rachel saw were Jackie and Gene. She hastily turned away, sidling towards the doorway.

A cheery call stopped her in her tracks.

"Rachel, over here, my dear. Come and join us!"

She wasn't sure how it happened, but she found herself accepting the Beamonds' invitation to join them. She ended up having lunch with what turned out to be two of the kindest, understanding and most optimistic people she had ever met. They were so easy to talk to and she found herself pouring out her life story to them.

If she hadn't actually been born pessimistic, she told them, her parents had certainly made her that way. They always saw the black side and never got excited about anything. No joyous anticipation was allowed anywhere near their world.

"If you don't expect much, you won't be disappointed," was their mantra.

Through her tears she explained how it had been with Ian. She'd really fallen for him, she said, explaining how he was constantly cheerful, the ready grin always there.

"I tried hard to match his optimism," she went on, "and to a certain extent it worked. I suppose his natural happiness rubbed off on me and for a while we were fine. I couldn't believe my luck in finding someone like Ian."

Rachel blew her nose hard.

"But then, as usual, the self-doubt started creeping in. This was too good to be true! Why was he with me when he could have anybody? This couldn't last! When he started telling me he had to work late it was the last straw.

"'You've got somebody else, haven't you?' I remember screaming at him," Rachel said. "He told me he hadn't, that he loved me, but that I was driving him away. He couldn't understand why I couldn't be happy.

"I can't understand it either. Why couldn't I do that?" Rachel questioned. "Why couldn't I explain to him the blackness that overcomes me whenever something good happens in my life?"

"But, my dear," Gene said, "it really doesn't work like that. You make your own life and happiness, you know. Not your parents, not Ian. It all has to start with you. Nobody else can be responsible for how you are feeling."

"It isn't what happens to you in life, it's how you choose to deal with it," Jackie put in.

"Now, tell me." Gene looked deep into Rachel's eyes. "If I asked you to count your blessings, what could you come up with?"

"Nothing," Rachel whispered without hesitation.

"You're young and healthy," Gene pointed out mildly. "That's two things."

Rachel looked at the elderly Beamonds, both smiling at her, their walking frames standing beside them. She couldn't help smiling at the irony.

"You've got the most beautiful smile," Jackie said as mildly as her husband. "Your whole face lights up. Anyone would be lucky to be on the receiving end of that smile. Make sure it happens more often from now on," she went on, tempering her order with her own lovely smile.

"I've got somewhere to live. My little cottage," Rachel said, realising suddenly how lucky she was to have it. She felt an overwhelming urge to nurture it when she thought of all the people she dealt with in sub-standard accommodation, who would give their eye teeth for a cottage like hers.

"Now you're getting the idea," Jackie and Gene said at the same time. Laughing, they reached out and squeezed Rachel's hands. "It won't be easy at first, my dear, but just try thinking positive thoughts and counting your blessings, however small. You won't believe the difference it will make to your life."

RACHEL looked round her neglected little cottage and felt something she'd only felt occasionally in her life. Hope. Hope that she could actually turn things around. All she had to do was to try to think happy and positive thoughts, and count her blessings.

Starting with her cottage. That was hers, her sanctuary. She wasn't under any illusions as to how difficult it would be for her to change the habit of a lifetime, but she desperately wanted to try. She wanted to radiate happiness like those two wonderful people she'd met today. That was worth striving for, surely, however much effort it took.

And Ian had said he loved her despite everything. It was, after all, she who had driven him away. She could and would change, she vowed now. After that, who knew what the future might hold for them both?

*　*　*　*

"That's been another good day, my dear." Gene kissed his wife goodnight.

"It has indeed, darling." Jackie returned his kiss and reflected, as she often did, how Gene had turned her life around.

She had been just the same as Rachel 10 years ago. Widowed, childless, morose, fed up with life and cursing the arthritis that was slowly crippling her. Then she'd met Gene at the arthritis clinic at the local hospital and it had changed her life. He'd struck up a conversation with her, and by the end of it she was feeling marginally better. He had taken her for a coffee, and then persuaded her to have lunch with him.

She learned his wife had died young but had blessed him with two lovely children, which had helped him to move on.

"How do you stay so cheerful?" she had asked curiously.

"Well, my dear." He'd grinned at her, those piercing blue eyes gazing into hers. "I reckon it would be a thousand times worse to be in pain *and* miserable. I met a pretty marvellous guy early on in my adult life, around the time my wife died. He taught me that I have a choice in how I feel. So I always choose to be happy. It's a challenge sometimes, believe me, but it is one thing over which I can have control. And it makes me even happier when I can create an opportunity to spread a little happiness wherever I go."

"So I'm a project, am I?" she'd asked, smiling in spite of herself.

"I have a feeling," Gene had replied quietly, "that you are going to be a very special project."

They had been together ever since.

"Rachel today," Jackie said as she drifted off to sleep. "I wonder who it will be tomorrow!" ■

Illustration by Philip Crabb/Thinkstockphotos.

Beneath Its Branches

by Susan Sarapuk.

THE whine of a chainsaw made Rosie's stomach flip. A tree was being cut down. She hated the sight of any tree being cut down. As she turned into the park she gave a groan. It was the horse chestnut! "Stop!" she cried out, but the workmen couldn't hear her above the whirring of the chainsaw. Large branches were piled up on the ground, waiting to be cut up and placed on the waiting truck.

"This is part of my life," she whispered, tearful. "You can't take my tree."

* * * *

Rosie was six when her parents first brought her to the park. They'd recently moved into the area. Moving up, she heard her mother say with pride, but all she could think of was how she was missing her old house, with the stream at the bottom of the garden and the ramshackle trees and bushes where she could make a den. Here they had only a small, tidy garden with no secret places.

"We'll go to the park on Saturday," her mother had promised.

She played on the swings while her parents sat on a bench, arm in arm, and watched her. Seeing her parents together made her feel warm and safe.

Her mother had packed a picnic.

"Let's find somewhere to eat lunch," she said.

"This looks good." Dad led them to a horse chestnut tree in full bloom. He spread out the blanket and they sat down.

Mum had made her favourite sausage and ketchup sandwiches and plenty of orange squash. Rosie munched contentedly and watched people playing cricket on the field, then she lay back on the blanket and gazed up through the yellow and lime leaves, watching the sun wink and sparkle through the gaps.

"We're going to make a good life here," Dad said with an arm about her mother's shoulders.

And if Rosie's dad said so, it must be true.

"Race you!" Pam started running as she said it. That just wasn't fair – she had a head start. She was faster than Rosie. Pam was her best friend. They were both eight years old.

"Thick as thieves, you two," her mother said.

Was she calling Rosie a thief? The only thing she'd ever stolen was Cara Lewis's packet of sherbet lemons. She'd felt guilty afterwards, but hadn't confessed to the crime because Cara was a big girl and would surely flatten her.

Rosie wasn't thick, either! Mrs Brant, the class teacher, had told her she was very good at sums and geography, and if she continued to work hard she'd be top of the class at the end of the year.

She had met Pam on her first day in the new school. She'd admired the doll the ginger-haired girl was playing with.

"Do you want to sit next to me at lunchtime?" Pam had asked.

After that they were inseparable.

Pam laughed as Rosie caught up with her under the horse chestnut tree.

"Ha! Bet you can't climb up here!" a voice said.

Rosie looked up to see a pair of knobbly-kneed legs dangling from a branch. A face peeped through the leaves and she recognised Chris Jennings from school.

"Of course we can!" She began to search for a foothold.

"Rosie, be careful." Pam wasn't so confident.

There were shouts of derision and Rosie realised that nearly half the class of boys were up the tree.

"Come on," Chris challenged.

Rosie didn't notice the bark scraping her knuckles or that it was a long way down as she searched for hand - and footholds and climbed the lower branches.

From there she climbed higher and higher, passing a couple of boys on the way up. She continued climbing until she reached Chris Jennings.

"Not bad for a girl," he conceded as she shuffled along the branch to sit beside him.

"You're mad!" Pam called up from the relative safety of a lower branch.

Maybe she was, but she'd proved to Chris Jennings that she could be as good as any boy. He seemed to take more notice of her after that.

THEY were arguing again. From what ten-year-old Rosie could glean there was a possibility her father might lose his job. Her mother had recently started going out to work to help things along.

Rosie missed her being there when she came home at the end of the school day. She had to let herself into the house and then not open the door to anyone until her mother came home an hour later. She wished it could be like the old days when they sat laughing and picnicking under the horse chestnut tree.

Her parents were still arguing as she appeared in the doorway.

"Stop it!" she cried.

They both looked up.

"Rosie." Her mother reached out.

"Stop it!" she said again, before turning and running out the front door.

It had started to rain and she didn't have a coat. Rosie ran into the park. She looked for shelter.

She made her way to the horse chestnut tree and huddled close to its familiar, soothing trunk, the leaf cover protecting her from the worst of the rain. She listened to the raindrops on the leaves, smelled the wet earth, and sighed. This tree had been here for 200 years. She liked that. Even though the world around her might be changing, some things went on no matter what.

She didn't know how long she stayed there, but when she looked up, her mother was approaching through the rain.

"Here." She held out Rosie's raincoat. "Put this on. You'll catch your death."

"How did you know I was here?"

"When you weren't at Pam's I guessed this would be the next place."

"Mum, are you and Dad going to split up?" Rosie asked tentatively.

Her mother folded her into an embrace.

"I hope not, sugar. Lots of parents go through sticky times. Now, come home and get out of those wet clothes.

＊　＊　＊　＊

Rosie lay back on the warm ground and gazed up at the gold and brown rustling canopy overhead. From time to time leaves fell in a confetti-like shower all around her. She was fourteen.

"Oh, my favourite!" Pam suddenly declared and turned up the radio at her side. "Ryan likes this, too."

Pam had her first boyfriend. They'd met at a disco at the beginning of term.

"So, what shall I wear tonight?"

"Your green dress?"

"I dunno. Maybe I ought to wear black. Black is sophisticated and slimming."

"Are you going to wear heels?"

"Of course."

Rosie looked over the field. There was a football match in progress.

"You'll have a boyfriend soon." Pam sat up. "Then we can go out together."

"Maybe."

"Chris Jennings likes you."

Rosie blushed and changed the subject. They talked about clothes and make-up and pop music, the way they did every Saturday afternoon. People began to disperse at the end of the match.

"Hiya, girls!" Chris Jennings strolled up in his muddy kit.

"Good game?" Rosie shielded her eyes against the low autumn sun.

"Not bad. What are you doing?"

"Listening to the radio, obviously," Pam said drily.

Rosie exchanged a glance with Chris. He looked as awkward as she felt.

"Well, see ya." He waved, turned and walked away.

"He was going out with Elle Ascott for a while," Pam confided. "But he's not any more. You should ask him out."

"No way!"

"Hey, Jennings!" Pam called out. "Bet you can't climb this tree still!"

"Wanna bet?" He looked at Rosie. "I'll do it if you will."

She watched him scurry up the trunk. It had been years since she'd attempted to climb the horse chestnut. She was a teenager now, and far too sophisticated. She searched for the old footholds and the memory of how to climb the tree came back. She felt like a tomboy again as she followed Chris Jennings.

"Did it!" she said triumphantly as she reached his side at the top.

"Never saw the view from here like this."

Rosie followed his gaze through the sparse leaf cover. People were streaming back to their cars and she could see the new estate laid out beyond the park's perimeters.

"You're OK, Rosie." He suddenly turned to her. "Do you want to come to the cinema with me some time?"

"OK."

✳   ✳   ✳   ✳

Rosie and Chris shared their first kiss under the horse chestnut tree. Now fifteen, she and Chris had been spending more and more time together. One day he suggested they take a walk through the park.

"I love this place."

Rosie sighed as she thought back to that first day her parents had brought her here. Despite their rocky patch a few years ago they were still together and she knew she was lucky.

"We must have a picnic some time." She turned to Chris to find him watching her intently.

"There's something else we must do first." His voice sounded husky, nervous, as he cupped her face in his hands and placed his mouth on hers.

Rosie had never been kissed before, not properly, and it was both a shock and a stirring.

He must have known how special this place was to her. She was glad she'd experienced her first kiss here and that it had been with him . . .

＊　＊　＊　＊

Only when there was a break in cutting did the workmen see Rosie frantically waving her arms.

"Stay back, love," one of them warned. "It's not safe."

"You can't cut this tree down!" Rosie wailed. "It's our tree!"

The image of the day Chris had asked her to marry him came into her mind. They'd both been home from university for the holiday.

"You'll meet someone new when you're away," her mother had said.

But Rosie hadn't wanted to. Chris was the only man for her.

"Meet you under the tree," he'd said on the phone.

When she saw him walking towards her, her heart was overwhelmed with love. Before he even greeted her he went down on one knee.

"Rosie, will you marry me?"

There was only one answer.

So now she knew she couldn't lose the tree!

DON'T worry, love, we're only pruning it," the workman said. "I reckon it'll be here for another couple of hundred years."

Rosie sighed with relief. Only then was she aware of the tears on her cheeks.

"What's going on, you mad woman? Abandoning your husband and child!"

Rosie turned to see Chris pushing Anjelica's pushchair. Then he saw the tree.

"It's OK, they're just pruning it." Rosie felt the comfort of her husband's arm around her waist.

"It's where we had our first kiss!" Chris called. "And where I proposed!"

The man holding the chainsaw saluted him.

Rosie laid her head on Chris's shoulder, and as she looked at the freshly pruned tree she made a wish that, to her daughter, it would be as important as it had been to her. ∎

Warwick Castle

NESTLING on a bend in the River Avon, Warwick Castle is everyone's idea of a traditional mediaeval castle. Built on a grand scale and dominating its surroundings, the castle occupied a strong defensive position, atop a steep sandstone bluff, with the river on one side.

The original wooden motte-and-bailey structure, dating from the time of William the Conqueror in 1068, was later developed into the substantial stone edifice that can be seen today. The ownership of the castle passed through the hands of several noble families. During the 13th century, the castle was even used to imprison the King, when Richard Neville, 16th Earl of Warwick, was involved in a plot to depose Edward IV.

The Earls were early adopters of the idea of opening their home to the paying public and the castle has been a popular destination for many years, with servants initially acting as guides. One of its many attractions was the collection of armoury, which was said to rival that of the Tower of London. Having passed from private ownership in 1978, it is now a major tourist attraction hosting events and activities that help to bring the castle's mediaeval history alive for visitors of all ages. ■

93

Carry On, Nurse

by Em Barnard.

IT was a Sunday morning and I'd gone to the open kitchen door for some fresh air while cooking lunch. Stan was gardening, on his knees edging a difficult corner of lawn with his shears before the promised rain, when suddenly our young granddaughter Wendy ran up and plonked a doll on his neck. Stan often carried Wendy or her dolls on his shoulders.

"Daisy wants a ride, Standad!"

He leaped back with a jump and I knew he'd cut his finger. A minute later he was at the sink, blood dripping from the gash on his index finger.

"Leave it now, Stan." I pulled it from under the tap. "Let it congeal and the bleeding will stop."

When I turned from the sink Wendy was standing in the doorway to the hall, clutching Daisy to her, eyes full of fear.

Stan winked.

"It's not your fault, darling. It's just a little cut. It doesn't hurt."

"In that cupboard, Wendy, you'll find the first-aid box." I pointed. "It's green. Would you get it for me?"

I watched her struggle to lift the box while still holding Daisy. Poor Daisy. That doll had more cracks on her head than a skittle and now received another as Wendy released her, needing two hands to grip the box.

Wendy trotted over and watched me dress the finger, fretful but fascinated.

"There. You take Standad into the lounge and sit him down, and I'll make him some tea."

"This way, Standad." She took his good hand and tugged on him.

We often had Wendy with us on a Sunday to give her parents a day to themselves. Today they'd gone to watch her other grandad playing bowls. Wendy soon had the toys that she kept with us strewn around the rooms and garden of our bungalow.

I walked into the lounge with a mug of sweet tea. Wendy was sitting beside Stan, both of them staring at his cocooned finger.

"Will it be well tomorrow, Standad?"

"It's well enough now, Wendy. In fact, I ought to go and put my tools away."

"I'll do that." I pushed him back down as he went to stand. "Drink this and rest a while."

"Yes, Standad, you rest a while."

Suddenly I could hear my daughter at that age when I cut my finger on an open tin. I turned in the doorway.

"What you need, Wendy, is a nurse's uniform! I made one for your mum when she was your age. I'll get it from the loft after dinner. Then you can take care of Standad."

AFTER lunch, I mopped the kitchen floor. Stan was watching the grand prix. Wendy was rattling her doll's buggy with a "vroom, vroom" up and down the tiled hallway, drowning out the TV commentary.

She stopped in the kitchen doorway.

"When are you going in the loft to get the nurse's dress for me?"

"When I've finished this." I reached down

Illustration by Kirk Houston/Thinkstockphotos.

for a teddy in red nightie and cap which was propped against the fridge. I set him on the table.

"You pop in the lounge and check Standad's pulse. A good nurse is always checking her patient."

I mopped the last remaining quarter, stumbling on three pencils and a green plastic frog. I put the mop away and stepped into the hall.

Spotting me, Wendy dropped Stan's wrist and ran to me.

"Are you going in the loft now, Nana?"

Stan was suddenly behind me.

"Let me go." He kicked aside a roller-skate to help me drag the ladder down.

"You don't know where to look. Plus you might stub that finger and make it bleed again."

I clattered up the ladder. Minutes later I passed Stan a carrier bag.

"Show me, Standad!" Wendy jumped impatiently beside Stan and they went into the lounge.

I stepped down, so busy watching them that I never saw the roller-skate. My foot found it and next I was clutching the ladder in a mad dance. Once my foot twisted free of the skate I clung to the ladder, my ankle pulsing with pain.

I limped along to the kitchen, hoping I'd not be spotted, not wanting to spoil Wendy's enjoyment. But I'd forgotten the wet floor. I skidded. I grabbed for a chair and with a shriek and a clatter went down.

Stan came running.

"Viv!"

"Help me up, please. But mind the floor. It's wet."

Once I was in a chair, Stan eyed me.

"You sure you're OK, Viv?"

"Yes."

Wendy ran in.

"Do you need a nurse, Nana?" she asked. The navy dress with its white apron and Red Cross on the bib fitted her a treat. And with her white winged cap slipping towards her right ear, she was a picture.

"I sure do," I said, rubbing my elbow. It tingled right down to my fingertips, while my ankle pulsed with pain as if not to be outdone.

"Let me do it, Standad," she said as Stan wrung out a wet tea towel.

He showed her how to wrap it round my ankle.

"Standad, you take Nana into the lounge to rest. Then I have to do your finger 'cause it's all soggy now."

Sitting side by side on the sofa, the sound low on the telly, we were bandaged by Wendy. Stan got his head and two knees bandaged and I had both elbows and both ankles. I'd pushed for a normal bandage for my painful ankle, which I helped Wendy bind. She was still playing the conscientious nurse, not allowing us to move. It was nice just to rest our sore bones, really.

Wendy helped Stan dress his finger, tying a big bow on it. I murmured to Stan that I couldn't half drink a cuppa. Wendy was across the lounge, bandaging up toys with scarves and ribbons.

"I'll get the tea, Viv."

As he stood up Wendy ran to him.

"Sit down, Standad. You're sick!"

"My brain's slowing down. I have to keep moving to speed it up. Nana is feeling weak, too, so let's make some tea. I'll need your shoulder to lean on."

Sausage rolls and fancies were brought to me on a plate. Wendy carried in Stan's while he made the tea.

WE were half asleep by the time the doorbell rang at six o'clock.

"Remember, Stan," I said as Wendy ran to let them in. "Our injuries are fake. I don't want Carol worrying."

Moments later Wendy tugged her mother into the lounge.

"See?" She pointed at us. "They're ill so I can't go home."

"Whatever's happened?" Carol hurried over.

Ray held back, hearing the story from his daughter.

"It's Wendy playing nurses," I whispered as Wendy showed off her uniform. Carol smiled, reassured.

"We'd best take her off your hands."

"No!" Wendy ran to us. "I have to stay to check on my patients."

"We can call in tomorrow, pet."

Carol reached a hand to her daughter but Wendy stepped back. Hands behind her, she shook her head.

"Come on, Wendy." Carol tried again with a look that brooked no argument.

Wendy cuddled into me. I was always her last hope.

I was wondering on the best way out of this when there was a clatter and yelp from the hall. When we reached him Ray was sitting on the doormat.

"My wrist!" He was cradling it in his hand, the skate I'd danced on beside him.

I looked at Stan.

"I thought you picked that up?"

"I did. I put it on the dresser."

Then we caught Carol's quizzical expression, and we realised Ray had picked up on our play-acting.

"Quick, Wendy, more bandages," I ordered while she was staring at her dad, open-mouthed.

Moments later she was running up to her dad with a new neat roll from the first-aid kit.

As she wrapped the arm, Ray placed a hand on his brow in a dramatic gesture.

"By the time I've driven home, I shall need an awful lot of pampering."

"Come on, Daddy. Let's get you in the car."

We all smiled, for that phrase was used on Wendy many a time. We watched her perfect her nursing skills by helping him stand and then hold his bandaged wrist carefully.

Our goodbyes said, with a reminder from Wendy to carry on resting, Stan and I waved the family off and traipsed back into the lounge, bandages flapping like a couple of tired zombies. We sat down and unravelled our dressings.

"I really thought Ray had hurt that wrist," Stan said.

"So did I. But it was a great way of getting Wendy to go home without tears and tantrums."

"I'll tell you what, Viv, I don't want another day like this."

"Me, neither." I stood up to go and fix supper.

"Viv, come here. Look which film's about to start!"

From the doorway I stared at the television screen.

"I think that would finish our day nicely."

As the opening credits to "Carry On, Nurse" rolled, I limped out from the kitchen, smiling. ▨

I'd Like To Know...

Sit back and enjoy this classic selection of vintage queries from the lovely readers of the "Friend"!

Q **I REMEMBER** Adam Faith as an actor and I used to love watching him in the TV drama "Budgie". My older sister, however, remembers him as a pop singer and insists that he had various hits in the early 60s. She can't, however, remember any of the songs he sang. Can you help?

– Mrs M.T., Troon.

A **ADAM FAITH**, born Terry Nelhams-Wright in 1940, was an English singer and actor. He was one of the most charted acts of the 1960s and had hits with "What Do You Want?", "Poor Me", "Someone Else's Baby" and "Don't That Beat All". He had a total of 24 chart entries, but turned his back on singing in 1968 to concentrate on acting. "Budgie" ran from 1971-72 and starred Adam Faith as an ex-con who was trying, not too successfully, to go straight. He also starred with Zoë Wanamaker in the TV series "Love Hurts" from 1992-94. Adam sadly died of a heart attack in 2003.

. . . .

Q **I'VE** just bought my daughter-in-law a pendant of jet from Whitby. Can you tell me more about this mineral and if it is mined anywhere else in the world?

– Mrs V.T., Leeds.

A **JET** is a minor gemstone and considered to be a mineraloid as opposed to a true mineral because it has an organic origin. Jet is a product of decaying wood that has been placed under extreme pressure. The jet found at Whitby is approximately 182 million years old and became popular as a gemstone during the reign of Queen Victoria, when she wore it as part of her mourning dress. Jet can be found in many countries – France, Spain, the USA, Turkey, China, Germany and India, to name but a few.

Illustration by Mandy Dixon/Thinkstockphotos.

She Who Dares

by Elizabeth Cook.

WHO did you say?" I asked my friend Lyn as I set the tray on the café table.

"Joanne Reid. She sent me an e-mail. Found me through our old school webpage. She's coming home. What I mean is, she and her family are leaving Australia to live back here."

The three of us had been friends in secondary school, back in the Sixties. And although Joanne was more Lyn's friend than mine, they'd lost touch over recent years.

I took the coffees from the tray.

"It's more than forty years since her and her fella – what was his name?"

"Paul."

"Since they married and left on those ten-pound tickets."

Lyn nodded.

"She wants us to meet up in London next month for a girlie reunion. And as we've a trip to London on our bucket list, I thought it would fit in a treat."

Living in Norwich, Lyn and I often went on day trips to London in our youth, and recapturing those days was on our list. Our "start living" bucket list had been created on my sixty-fifth birthday a few months back, at a surprise party held at Lyn's home. It was well into that warm May evening and we were curled up on the sofa in her summerhouse.

We were reminiscing, wondering where the years had gone, when we realised how many of our dreams had been unfulfilled, so we decided that it was time to capture some of them before we were too old to do so.

However, it was the wine that had madly fortified us to add things to the list, like bursting through our fear barriers. For Lyn it went back to her childhood when she was always sick on coach trips. We'd often wanted to go on the evening mystery tours that ran locally, but Lyn didn't dare chance it.

But now she had conquered her fear. Half an hour into the ride her sickness hadn't shown itself. I told her she'd probably outgrown it after all this time. And we didn't have to get off and jump in with our fellas, driving behind. I could see the relief in her eyes once she stepped off the coach at the country inn, and hear her delighted laughter after the return journey. I wanted a share of that, too.

My fear was heights, which again compromised the family holidays we shared together. So I made up my mind that on our London trip I'd go on the London Eye. But now Joanne had entered the frame. When the three of us were fifteen we'd gone on a Ferris wheel, and when it stopped at the top Joanne had rocked us to tipping point. I could picture her now, laughing, a manic look in her eyes, and my fear of heights had stuck with me ever since.

L OOK, meeting Joanne will have nothing to do with us going on the Eye," Lyn assured me.

I must have looked thoughtful, for the next thing I knew she was making a funny face at me.

I laughed.

"Not like that, like this." Dad had perfected them way before Les Dawson and had taught me from toddler age. And now I was teaching my grandchildren, and some grown-ups, too!

Lyn chuckled.

"So is that a yes to coming to London, and meeting Joanne?"

"And doing the Eye," I added. "But just the two of us in case I make a fool of myself."

"Great, Chrissie. You'll be fine, I just know it."

We'd booked a small hotel close to Liverpool Street Station for a long weekend, leaving our fellas pondering over the idea of a bucket list of their own.

Saturday had been great. It was like reclaiming our youth, shopping in Oxford Street being top of our list. The frivolity and daring of those carefree teenage days when the sun seemed to shine endlessly – as it had today – were happy memories recalled. The only thing missing was the Sixties' atmosphere; Carnaby Street, bobbies on bicycles, mini-skirts and mods.

"What's up, Lyn?" I asked, as we came out of a theatre into the warm, dark evening of a carnival atmosphere West End. "There were times during that comedy when I would look your way and you were right serious."

"I didn't want to spoil your evening. Joanne phoned earlier." Lyn paused. "She's doing the Eye with her family tomorrow and suggested we all go up together. I tried to say no, but . . ." She looked at me anxiously.

I laughed and swung my arm in hers.

"Nothing's going to spoil it for me – not even Joanne. Come on, let's go to the Festival Hall for a coffee, and see how much it's changed."

FROM below, the London Eye resembled a giant space station in its tubular construction.

"There's Joanne!" Lyn cried, and with a swirl of her pink dress weaved through the tourists. Gripping my shoulder bag close to me, I followed, my heart thudding over the coming ride.

"Hi, there!" Joanne met Lyn in a tight, swinging hug. "It's so great to see you. And Chrissie, too." She gripped my hand. "After all these years, why, you've not changed at all."

"Nor have you," Lyn said with a grin.

"There are a few highlights to camouflage the grey these days, though," Joanne confided, scrunching her fair curls. "Oh, there's Paul, we must get aboard. We can talk as we go."

I took a heartening breath. As we stepped aboard the capsule, at its snail-pace mode, my first surprise was the size of it. The capsules were advertised as big enough for small dinner parties and weddings. Fearfully, I made a dash for the centre seats and sat clutching my shoulder bag in the lap of my gentian blue dress. Joanne had gone to bring Paul over to meet us. Between folk wandering past me, I could see the River Thames sparkling in the sunshine.

"Paul, do you remember Lyn and Chrissie?" Joanne asked her husband.

"You were at our wedding?" he asked.

We nodded, said a word or two.

"Once we're settled in London," Joanne began, "we're coming to spend a week in Norwich going round the old haunts. We'll have to meet up at the seaside just like the old days."

"The Ferris wheel's not there now," I heard myself say, but she'd swung away to see to her daughter, who had waved a hand. Paul smiled and followed her.

Seeing Lyn frowning at me, I began to ramble.

"Did you know it takes thirty minutes to do a rotation, twice as fast as a sprinting tortoise? I did some research. In fact, so far, I'm OK. Look, isn't it a glorious view?"

Many were standing close to the glass and I felt safely cocooned in my centre seat. Now and then, as they moved on, I caught a glance of London sinking below us. It felt safer thinking of it that way.

"Why don't you go to the windows, Lyn?"

"I'm fine." She shook her head.

"Just go and enjoy it. Don't worry about me. I'm going to take some photos on my mobile."

M Y hands were shaky at first, but soon they steadied as I became wrapped up in snapping Lyn, the view, Joanne and her family. Her young grandson was leaning, his hands against the glass, looking down on the sprawling city below. A tingling crept up my legs as my imagination stood with him on that edge, viewing the metropolis.

I swung away and found Joanne's granddaughter. The tot was leaning into her mother, clutching her hand, eyes wide with fear. I lowered my camera. As her eyes met mine, I made a funny face. Instantly she giggled, catching her mother's attention.

"That was a nice thing to do." Lyn sat beside me.

Joanne hefted her granddaughter up and brought her over.

"Tannie's a little upset by the height. She wants to sit with you because you made a funny face."

"Oh, I can make lots of funny faces. Would you like me to teach you?" I asked the little girl.

She nodded eagerly and sat beside me with her mother. Some minutes later, through the laughter of a group we'd gathered, someone shouted.

"We've reached the top!" There was a rush to the windows, everyone eager to snap London's concrete panorama.

"Come on, Lyn. Chrissie!" Joanne tugged us from our seats. "We must have a photo from the window. It is such a spectacular view." Joanne chained us with her arms, one on each side, and pressed us to the glass to look over the great expanse of London.

Instinctively I looked down. From my toes queasiness surged through me, powering round my head in pounding beats.

"Hey, stop trembling, Chrissie." Joanne laughed. "And stop pulling faces. We're not on that Ferris wheel now. I've never quite forgiven Lyn for rocking us that time."

"It wasn't me," Lyn protested, suddenly catching my accusing eye.

"And I certainly wasn't pulling funny faces," I retorted.

Joanne laughed.

"Oh, yes, you were, Chrissie. You were pulling such hilarious faces I just creased up laughing. It was that which helped me cope. At least it sorted out my fear of heights. You don't know how scared I was before we went on that wheel. But no way was I letting on in front of my two best friends." She swung us round to face Paul with his camera. Her arms went over our shoulders. "Smile. Nicely now, Chrissie."

As I returned to my seat beside Tannie, Lyn was suppressing giggles. I ignored her and went back to teaching little Tannie, her attention held in trying to imitate me, while we collected further onlookers. We were all surprised when it was time to disembark.

YOU did it." Lyn hugged me as we stood on the embankment. "I'm so pleased for you. How do you feel?"

"I quite enjoyed it actually. Yes, I did feel queasy when Joanne pushed us into that window. But then, I'm wondering if it's just things like fairground wheels which are wide open to the elements that drive my fear. You sure it wasn't you who rocked us that time?"

"No. Truly, Chrissie. It was probably the lot of us, just having fun like kids do. Fancy, though, all these years you've been scared of heights, but right at the start you helped cure Joanne of hers. And now, in a way, she's returned the favour."

"I don't remember pulling faces."

"I don't either. But it's what we do when we're scared, it's what these rides are all about. Except that when you pull a face, Chrissie, it's sheer genius."

Joanne stepped up to us.

"That was great. Thank you for what you did for Tannie, Chrissie." She hugged me. "Come on, the family's off to that café over there. You will join us, won't you? We can have a good chinwag just like old times, the three of us together." She put herself in the middle and weaved her arms through ours. "Tomorrow I feel I want to go higher still. And I want you both to come, too.

"No, not the Shard!" She laughed. "The Planetarium. So there's no need for face-pulling there, Chrissie, even if you do get a crick in your neck."

Suddenly I was laughing. Lyn and I had that on our list, too!

"We were going there ourselves, weren't we, Lyn?"

She picked up on my approval.

"Yes, we'd love to come, Joanne."

And, with friendships reunited, we headed into the café. ■

Simply Swellegant!

by Amanda Young.

WEE Sadie Perjink, born Sarah Davidson, sat with the four people she loved best in all the world, around the table in her family's little kitchen. These were her ma and da, her uncle Hammy MacDougal, a long-time favourite, and her dear new auntie Mirren, formerly known strictly as Miss Murdoch. The remains of a splendid tea, tribute to her ma's deft ways with her range oven, littered the table. The chatter had been worse than the monkey house at Edinburgh Zoo, and the laughter non-stop.

The centre of all of this jollity was to be found in Uncle Hammy, who had been able to climb the stairs to the Davidsons' home, albeit with the help of a pair of stout crutches, for the first time since he broke his leg months before. On this special day Mary Davidson had arranged a little meal to celebrate the long-postponed engagement between Hammy and Mirren.

Hammy MacDougal was a large, jolly man with red cheeks and a heart of twenty-two-carat gold. Now, he clinked his teaspoon on his cup.

"I'm calling this meeting to order. Be quiet, the lot of you!"

The others fell silent in obedience. Unfortunately, Hammy was no great shakes as a public speaker, and after a lot of harrumphing and blowing his nose he hadn't got out a single word. It was then that Mirren Murdoch took a hand, taking pity on Hammy, with whom she had rekindled their old love affair thanks to Sadie's well-intentioned meddling.

"Come on, you great eejit! Get on with it!" The obvious fondness in her tone took any sting out of the remark. "What he wants to talk about are the arrangements for our wedding."

Sadie clapped her hands with joy, for she was to be flower girl, and her auntie Mirren's sole attendant.

Hammy went even redder.

"Och! This is no' ma sort of thing at all. You say it, Mirren."

"It may be just as well if I do." That lady was used to taking charge of things, and her future husband would be no exception. "It's to be a quiet affair."

Illustration by Jim Dewar/Thinkstockphotos.

"Aye!" Hammy interjected. "We don't want too many people reminding us what a couple of gowks we were."

Mirren nodded her agreement and went on.

"Just a few people, very close to us. The minister has agreed to come to the house in the late morning. There's to be a wee reception there, too. But afterwards just the five of us are going to a matinée at the theatre."

"The theatre!" Wee Sadie Perjink was ecstatic.

"Yes. We're going to see an operetta."

"What's a noperretta?" Sadie asked blankly.

"It's a story with music and dancing," Mirren Murdoch tried to explain.

"Like the pantymine?"

Sadie's da always took them to the Princess Theatre near Gorbals Cross at Christmas to see the wonderful pantomime.

"Haud yer wheesht!" her ma interjected. "Let Mirren speak."

"Then we're going for tea at Danny Brown's."

Though chastened, Sadie couldn't help but ask, "Where's that?"

"It's a restaurant nearby."

"A restyrant!"

SADIE was once again stunned into silence. She had only ever thought of helping to bring this pair back together. She was a movie fan and at the pictures such stories ended on a tender kiss and a promise to be for ever true. The events that followed in real life had never occurred to her. And she hadn't heard the half of it yet . . .

"Before that day, Sadie will have to get a dress for the occasion," Mirren added.

"Oh, Ma. Will we get a pattern from the Misses Sheddens?"

These spinster ladies kept a haberdasher's shop just two streets away. Mary Davidson was an expert on her sewing machine, and visited these ladies frequently for thread, materials and cut-out patterns for dresses and skirts for herself and her daughter.

Mirren Murdoch held up her hand.

"Indeed she will not. Mary, I have a great regard for your dress-making ability, but on this occasion you can sit back. I – we –" she nodded at a beaming Hammy "– insist on buying Sadie's dress. You and I, young lady, will have a Saturday morning in town. We shall visit the best shops there and I shall pick my outfit, and we'll find you a dress at the same time," she promised.

"Crivvens!" Sadie's mind filled with pictures of the weddings she had seen. "You mean I'll get a white dress with shoes and a wee bag to match?"

"Of course you shall!"

When Mirren Murdoch spoke in that sort of tone it was a done deal. The adults set about the detailed arrangements to be put in place, and Sarah Davidson sank into unusual silence. A careful observer would have noticed her little frown of worry, and indeed one person turned his gaze upon her and watched closely, for behind the jollity and his breezy manner Hammy MacDougal was a shrewd observer of human nature. Since he had thought he would never get to marry Mirren, he had put all thoughts of a family of his own out of his mind. He was daft about weans, however, and instead poured all his affection on Sadie.

L ATER, when the time came to break up the party, Hammy spoke. "I'll go on ahead, Mirren. It'll take me a minute or two to get down to the street. You and Mary can have a wee extra gossip." Then he turned to Sadie's da. "Here, Willie! See's an oxter doon they stairs. They're gey steep for me the noo." He winked at Sadie. "When I'm a' better, I'll gie him a race and beat him hollow."

Sadie scoffed at the idea that anyone could beat her da at anything.

At the bottom of the steps the men paused for breath.

"Och, here, Willie, I've forgotten my crutches. Will ye go on up and fetch them to me?"

Grumbling mildly, Sadie's da climbed back up the stairs. Hammy watched until he was out of earshot.

"I would like to come shopping with you, wee lass, but I'm no' able yet. But ye'll have a great time wi' your auntie Mirren."

"I'm sure I will," his goddaughter said in a tone that didn't sound heartfelt.

"Now, wee wifie, there's something wrong. I can't imagine what it is. But it was your visit to Mirren's, when you told her I had broken my leg, that brought her to my hospital bed and the pair of us to our senses. We're both very grateful to you. You must let me try to right whatever is wrong with you."

Sadie was glad to have someone to confess to.

"Well, ye see, I told a wee lie at the time. I thought there was no harm in it, but now that I've to get a flower girl's dress and go to the theatre and have my tea in a restyrant and everything, I'm not sure I deserve it all. Telling lies isny right."

Hammy MacDougal couldn't believe his ears.

"You, tell a lie? I dinna believe it."

"I did. I said that you kept a picture of Mirren in the back of your watch."

"The photo in my watch? But that's –"

"I know, it's a photie of your best pigeon there. She's called Mirren, too."

There was a great bellow of mirth. Hammy MacDougal went from red to purple in the face and laughed until tears poured down his face.

"Oh, I'm sair frae laughin'. Guid sakes, wee lassie, that's the best joke ever. Oh, but you're a tonic."

He drew a fancy great Paisley-patterned handkerchief out of his top pocket, and wiped his face. At that moment the other adults could be heard at the top of the stairs.

"Now, before they come doon, let me assure you that you havenae to give this another thought. Mebbe it was a lie, but it wisnae a big black one, just a tottie wee white one. And they are quite allowed. We'll make this our secret. No need to mention this to anyone else."

When Willie Davidson and the two ladies came downstairs to join them, the final arrangements were made for the visit to town the very next Saturday. Feeling absolved from all sense of blame, Wee Sadie Perjink beamed like a sunbeam. But on his way home that night Hammy MacDougal had a thoughtful air.

T HE following Saturday Miss Mirren Murdoch and Miss Sarah Davidson boarded a tramcar on their way to town. Both were in full fig for such an important occasion. Mirren had on a hat and a fox fur, and carried a handbag the size of a portmanteau, while Sadie matched her auntie in smartness, having on her good grey coat set off by tammy and gloves in Fair Isle pattern.

Auntie Mirren outlined the plan.

"I'm not quite sure what I want, so we shall have to do a bit of leg work. We'll have a cup of tea mid-morning and review progress. How does that sound?"

Sadie turned to face her auntie, searching for the proper word to do justice to the occasion.

"That sounds just swell." The Americanism was all the rage in films, and Sadie wasn't sure why her auntie burst out laughing.

"Did I say something wrong?"

"No, my dear lassie. You said it just right."

The huge array of famous department stores that made Glasgow the best shopping centre in the Empire outside of London was rarely visited on Sadie's trips to town with her ma. This time was different. Auntie Mirren started at Wylie Hill's at the bottom of Buchanan Street, then crossed the street and worked her way through McDonald's and Wylie Lochhead's.

It was clear she was well known to the ladies in charge, and Sadie sat happily on a seat, absorbing the upmarket surroundings and the lovely dresses brought out for inspection and to try on.

"It's to be a quiet wedding in the house," Mirren Murdoch explained, "so I want something simple yet elegant."

Elegant. There was a word to savour. Wee Sadie Perjink stored it away for future use. And as they worked their way up to Sauchiehall Street that grand word became more and more appropriate. Pettigrew's, Copland and Lye, Daly's . . . each one seemed more swish than the last.

"Oh, but I'm leg-weary!" The older woman gasped. "I think it's time we had a break. Would you like some tea, Sadie?"

"Tea? I'm that wabbit I could drink a pot dry."

On their way upstairs to the tearoom at Daly's, Wee Sadie thought she could hear instruments tuning up. Looking around for the source, she was amazed to see three severe-looking ladies, one wearing pince-nez spectacles, getting ready to play for the customers on piano, violin and cello.

She stopped stock still.

"It's a baun'!" She gasped. "A real live baun' tae listen to as you drink your tea!"

Although the ladies looked stern, when they started to play their faces lit up, they became animated and the music they played was jolly and lilting. Sadie beat time as her auntie explained.

"They're playing a selection from the operetta we're going to see. 'The Chocolate Soldier'."

"The chocolate sodger?" Sadie was disbelieving. "Crivvens!"

The bride-to-be ordered elevenses for two, and Sadie sat enchanted as a three-tiered stand full of goodies was placed on the table.

The place was packed with ladies, all done up like Auntie Mirren. Looking around at them, Sadie was struck yet again by the difference between real life and that portrayed in the films she loved so much. She stored up every little detail for future reference.

"You aren't eating much, Sarah. I thought you were hungry?"

Wee Sadie Perjink helped herself to a French cake with pink icing.

"Oh, no. I'm having an elegant sufficiency."

There! She knew she'd find an occasion to use that phrase.

"It's just that a' they ongauns are so new to me. D'ye no' think that lady with the big fiddle between her knees will get bowly leggit in time?"

HAVING recharged their inner ladies, the pair went to visit the dress department. Once again the manageress and Sadie's auntie were clearly on familiar terms.

"How nice to see you, Miss Murdoch. How can I help you today?"

"I'm to be married in the autumn, Miss Martin. A small affair in the house. So I want something appropriate."

"I'm delighted for you, Miss Murdoch. We must indeed find you a special morning dress!"

She gestured to one of her assistants who scurried about, bringing frock after frock for approval. But Sadie's aunt could find nothing to her taste.

As usual, Sadie had been taking in every detail. Her attention was caught by a tailor's dummy wearing a two-piece costume in finest tweed. She wandered over to it and examined it carefully. The suit had a blue background, and woven through it was the most subtle of check patterns. But what really made it special were the collar, lapels, and the flaps to the patch pockets, which were of velvet in a deeper blue.

"See this costume, Auntie Mirren! Your eyes would fair go with this lovely colour."

Hammy MacDougal was never finished telling his bride-to-be how her deep blue eyes were the first thing that had attracted him to her. Intrigued, Mirren went to examine the costume.

"D'you know, Sarah, I think you might have come up with the right idea. What do you think, Miss Martin?"

The sales lady tutted in annoyance at herself.

"Why didn't I think of that? A tweed suit on an autumn morning. What could be more appropriate? I think this young lady has an eye for such things."

Sadie preened.

The tailoress was summoned, essential alterations were discussed and a fitting arranged for a few days later. Miss Mirren Murdoch was highly satisfied.

"Now we must find this wee lass a nice dress. She's to be my flower girl, you see."

"Could I suggest that the usual sort of white outfit won't go very well with this?" the tailoress ventured. "I propose we make a similar outfit for her. It would make a most unusual – and sophisticated – pairing."

Sophisticated! Miss Sarah Davidson was transported.

"It would look so smart. Besides, it would do for best for some time after. We could put a big hem and a false pleat in the skirt, to be let out in due course. When the jacket became too small the skirt would do very well with a twin set."

Whilst Miss Mirren Murdoch had set out to be as generous as possible to her new niece, this idea immediately appealed to her Scottish upbringing.

"What a sensible idea. But I promised her a white outfit," she said, dubious.

She needn't have worried. Wee Sadie Perjink had been raised with the same sort of background, and she saw at once the wisdom of such a decision.

Even more important, she now saw herself as elegant and sophisticated.

"Oh, Auntie Mirren." She searched for a word that would do justice to the situation. "I think that would be utterly swellegant!"

The whole day was recounted to Sadie's parents a dozen times, until Willie Davidson threw up his hands in despair.

"Ah'll be glad when that pair are hitched."

THREE months later, a small, happy group foregathered in Miss Mirren Murdoch's big parlour, waiting for the bride and her attendant to appear. When they did so there was a gasp of admiration. As Miss Mirren Murdoch handed her bouquet of white heather to her attendant, there were audible murmurs.

"Matching costumes? How original. And how lovely!"

"How grown up Sadie has suddenly become," someone said.

That young lady positively glowed.

The minister conducted a simple ceremony, all the more moving because every one of the small group knew how nearly this happy event had never occurred.

After the delightful buffet lunch that followed, the five intimates set off by taxi for the Alhambra theatre, where as a special treat Hammy had taken a box. Sadie got to sit at the front, leaning her elbows on the ledge. She watched the show, entranced.

She was fair carried away by the romance and glamour of the story. But, for the umpteenth time in the past few months, she was brought up sharp by the difference from real life. For although the box was wonderful for seeing the action close up, it also showed the truth behind the costumes and make-up. It became clear how the greasepaint was used so it could be made out at the farthest corner of the theatre.

She could also see what was going on in the wings. Actors waiting to come on chatted quietly and laughed as they waited for their cue.

DESPITE her uncle Hammy's reassurance, Sadie wondered again about her lie.

What she had done might have been all right in a film, or on stage, but in real life was it truly so? Sadie had a quick glance at the newlyweds, and was reassured by their obvious happiness. When this was mirrored on stage and the Chocolate Soldier and his sweetheart kissed, Sadie was satisfied that she had done the right thing.

"Well, did you enjoy that?" her da asked.

"It was absolutely unspeakable!" she enthused.

The theatre was only a short walk from Danny Brown's, but it took them through the heart of the city. It was dark by then, and the tramcars that rattled by were lit. The huge advertising signs, made up of hundreds of electric lightbulbs, winked in and out. The crush of people, the slight touch of frost, the wraith of autumn fog all wove a kind of magic and Sadie breathed deeply of the big city she loved so much.

When they reached Danny Brown's restaurant, Sadie Perjink received a further surprise, for this place was famous for its two-course teas.

"You mean I can have both fish and chips *and* ham and eggs?"

"Indeed you can," her ma assured her. "If you're sure you can eat it all."

Sadie's appetite had been sharpened to famish pitch by the excitement of these past few hours. She tucked in to such an extent her new skirt felt tight. At the end, they all sat back to enjoy one last cup of tea and have one final chat about the day's events.

"Just as well you winna have to break your leg again tae get married, Hammy. Was it really that that melted your heart, Mirren?" Willie joked.

"To tell the truth, it wasn't," Mirren MacDougal, as she now was, confessed. "Oh, I was right sorry to hear he had been badly hurt, but the thing that really got to me was when Sarah told me about the photograph."

"What photo?"

"Well, Sarah told me all about him keeping my photo in the back of his watch all of these years." She nodded at Sadie for confirmation but Sadie's face was a study in guilt. Mirren looked at her sternly. "That *is* what you told me?"

Sadie nodded dumbly.

The new bride turned to her husband.

"Hammy MacDougal, open your watch to me this very minute!" Her tone brooked no refusal.

Looking even more guilty than Sadie, Hammy fished his watch out from his waistcoat pocket.

"Now open it!"

"I could let you hear it chime?" he offered.

"I've heard it chime. I want it opened."

Hesitantly, Hammy inserted a fingernail under the cover and prized it open. There, on view to everyone, was the picture of his favourite racing pigeon, Mirren of Mugdock.

"Oh!" Mrs Hammy MacDougal gasped. Her disappointment was clear to see. Slowly she said, "I suppose I would have married you anyhow, but what a let down," she said. "How could you deceive me, Sarah?"

Sadie blinked away tears. Her ma and da, astounded at this turn of events, stared at aunt and niece. Then Uncle Hammy chimed in.

"Aye, Mirren. But you've got little faith. It's just as well I've enough for the pair of us!"

WITH that, he flicked aside the photo of the pigeon and revealed, underneath, a snapshot of a girl of the Twenties, with flapper skirt, cloche hat and all. It was clearly a young Mirren Murdoch.

That lady clapped her hands to her mouth in dismay.

"Oh, I'm that sorry ever to have doubted you, Hammy. And as for you, Sarah, please forgive me. I should have known you would never tell a lie, my dear."

There was a collective sigh from Sadie's parents at the passing of such an awkward situation, and the vindication of their daughter's truthfulness.

As Sadie looked wonderingly at her uncle Hammy, he closed one eye at her in a great big wink. ■

North Uist, Outer Hebrides

JUST 18 miles long and 12 miles wide, North Uist in the Outer Hebrides is a tiny gem set in the Atlantic. Idyllic views over a unique landscape make this a favourite destination for visitors thirsting for unspoiled natural beauty and blissful peace and quiet.

In the 2001 census, the island was home to fewer than 1,300 people, 300 of whom lived in and around the island's principal town, Lochmaddy. The main industries for centuries were fishing and agriculture, though tourism is now very important for the island's economy.

Many visitors come to see a natural habitat virtually unknown elsewhere, the flower meadows of coastal grassland bordering the sand dunes known as machair. Myriad small lochs or lochans dotted throughout the island's peat bogs reflect the sky, making a landscape unlike any other. Otters, corncrakes and a large grey seal colony draw wildlife enthusiasts to the island, while birdwatchers are catered for with the RSPB reserve at Balranald, where seasonal sightings of corn buntings, lapwings, turnstones and barnacle geese may be enjoyed. ■

Getting To Know You

by Rebecca Holmes.

THERESA was in her room, struggling with an essay, when she heard the crash. By the time she'd reached the first floor landing, Molly, one of her housemates, was already thundering up the stairs, her face nearly as red as her dyed hair.

"You are not going to believe what just happened!"

"What?"

"A cupboard fell off the kitchen wall!"

"Not the one with all the crockery?"

No wonder she'd heard it all the way from her attic bedroom.

Molly nodded.

"It's all over the floor."

Even though nearly four weeks had passed since Theresa had arrived here, everything still felt unreal.

Her mum had fussed, of course, the day her parents had dropped her off. At one stage Theresa had been worried Mum might cry, which would probably have set her off, but luckily that didn't happen. Dad was sort of gruff and jovial, which meant the occasion was getting to him, too. It was strange, really. With her brother having already gone to university a few years ago, this should hardly be a new experience for them.

"Well, it seems a good-sized house, and it looks as though it's been modernised quite well. It's certainly better than some of the places I stayed in when I was your age." Her dad's laugh had seemed forced. "The less said about some of those, the better!"

Unfortunately, Theresa hadn't secured a place in her university's halls of residence. Still, it had only taken seconds for her to fall in love with the house where a room was offered to her. Three steps led up to the solid front door of a Victorian semi with huge bay windows, standing in a row of similar houses along a tree-lined road in what would once have been a well-to-do area. The big draughty hall gave way to a ground-floor bedroom and a large, open-plan kitchen-cum-living room. Two more bedrooms and a voluminous bathroom made up the first floor, while the house was topped by a pair of attic rooms,

Illustration by Jim Dewar/Thinkstockphotos.

one of which was Theresa's, and a tiny second bathroom.

Large windows let in plenty of light, while the solid walls were probably more conducive to quieter nights than those on the campus, a bus ride away. Soon, though, she'd begun to wonder if it was all a bit too quiet, as well as isolated from where everything was happening. And shouldn't she have seen a bit more of her housemates by now?

* * * *

She had tried to describe her housemates on the phone to her parents.

"There's a big guy called Tony in the bedroom on the ground floor. He's doing geology, and I think he's got a Geordie accent."

"What do you mean, you think?" Mum had asked. "Haven't you chatted with him?"

"Well, he's a third-year, so he's busy, and you know I'm hopeless at recognising regional accents. Then there's Hans, who's Dutch and a post-grad student, and Molly who's a first-year like me and doing, um, politics."

That was a guess. Molly just looked the sort who'd be doing something like that, somehow, with her short, dyed hair and long, dangly earrings. Theresa didn't know what subject Hans was studying, either. He hardly seemed to be around the house.

"Who's in the other attic room, next to yours?"

"That's Su Linn. At least, I think that's her name. She's Chinese and she's very quiet, but she seems nice."

NOW, Hans and Su Linn materialised and headed downstairs with Theresa and Molly to inspect the damage. They found Tony already in the kitchen, starting to sweep up the mess on the floor.

"Watch where you're treading," he warned. "There are some nasty sharp edges."

Hans gave a low whistle as he carefully pulled the carcass of the cupboard away from where it still hung, swinging, held on the wall by one corner.

"We don't want this to land on someone and injure them," he said, in a surprisingly soft melodic accent.

The clink, clink of broken crockery as everyone gingerly picked out pieces and threw them into a cardboard box Tony had brought in accompanied Molly's rendition of the event.

"I was just at the sink filling the kettle when I heard this sliding noise behind me!" She had a habit of inflecting her words upwards at the end of sentences as if asking a question. "When I turned round, I saw the cupboard moving. There was nothing I could do to stop it."

"You'd have been mad to try," Tony assured her. "Better broken plates than broken bones. Anyway, it could have been worse."

He gestured towards the selection of plates, bowls and mugs by the sink.

"Maybe there's something to be said for students being rubbish at washing up."

As everyone laughed, even Su Linn, it struck Theresa that this was the first time all five of them had been together. It also struck her that she was glad she'd used her favourite plate for her meal of cheese on toast earlier. It meant that it was safely in her room, as were two of her mugs. Sadly, two of her side plates and another mug were among the casualties.

"I'll phone the landlady and tell her what's happened," Tony said as he swept up the last of the shards. "She's a nice person. She'll sort something out."

In next to no time, it seemed, they were all heading back to their rooms. Theresa couldn't help thinking it was a shame that no-one seemed inclined to stop and chat.

She tried to settle back down to her essay about the Victorian poets and how they'd influenced the philosophy of their time. Had any of them ever dreamed that one day an eighteen-year-old woman in skinny jeans would be sitting in an attic bedroom, with an animal print throw on the bed and a Benedict Cumberbatch poster on the wall, writing about the meaning of the lines over which they'd struggled?

Or should that be the other way round – that she was struggling over the lines they'd written? Maybe she wasn't up to this course after all. It didn't help that most of the lecturers went through everything so quickly, making it difficult to keep up and take notes.

Then there was the social side, or lack of one. Before coming here, Theresa had imagined sitting up with her new friends and talking into the early hours. Wasn't university supposed to be the sort of place where you found yourself, rather than feeling lost? Life outside the house hadn't lived up to its promise, either, once the novelty of her new surroundings had worn off.

No-one really seemed to talk much. It wasn't that they were unfriendly, just that once the standard topics of what A-Levels they'd done and where they came from had been covered, everyone seemed to run out of steam, by which time the lecture was starting anyway. When it ended, they went their own separate ways. Theresa was sure this would change if she could somehow break the ice, but that was more easily said than done.

Not that she told her parents any of this. They'd only be worried. Funnily enough, they were surprisingly quiet with news on their part. They asked lots of questions about what she was doing, but when she asked what was happening with them they'd just say, "Oh, the usual, you know."

At least next time she'd have something to tell them.

THANKFULLY, Theresa felt a lot brighter the next morning. That may have been down to a forget-me-not blue sky contrasting with the just-turning leaves of the sycamore outside her window. One of the things she loved about her attic room was the way she could look out, with her elbows on the narrow window-sill, at surrounding rooftops and the upper branches of nearby trees.

It could also have been the knock on her door. No-one had knocked on it until now.

"It's Tony from downstairs," a friendly Geordie voice called. "You needn't answer if you're not decent. I'm just letting you know we're having a house meeting at six. The landlady's away, but her son's going to call in on his way home from work. I thought it would be best if we were all present."

A house meeting? Theresa couldn't help grinning at the idea. There was something else to grin about, too. Today she actually had something different to talk about with whoever she sat next to in that morning's lecture. The story of their kitchen disaster would make a perfect ice breaker.

She got to the lecture theatre a few minutes early and sat next to a girl she'd said hello to a few times.

"You'll never guess what happened in my house yesterday."

The girl looked interested.

"What?"

The two of them were soon giggling as Theresa described the scene.

"My mum told me I should only bring old or cheap plates with me, in case some got broken," the student, who had introduced herself as Lindy, remarked. "It's very different from life at home, isn't it? Mind you, so are a lot of things here." She paused. "I hope you don't mind me asking, but what did you make of that essay? I'm finding it quite hard."

"Me, too. It's taking me ages," Theresa admitted.

"Oh, I'm so glad it's not just me. I didn't like to tell anyone in case it made me look a bit, you know, stupid. Everyone else seems so sure of what they're doing."

"I know what you mean," Theresa agreed. "I'm beginning to wonder if appearances are deceptive, though."

Their lecturer walked to the front at that moment and the room went quiet, but not before the two of them had made whispered arrangements to go to the students' union's cafeteria later.

FOR the house meeting Theresa wore a pretty new scarf she'd bought at lunchtime at a nearby vintage shop. It was a dusky pink, fringed and with sequins, and she'd known at once that it was perfect. Lindy had come shopping with her, and they'd both picked up some bargains in the process of chatting about clothes, their home lives and what their housemates were like.

The new scarf seemed to give Theresa more confidence and make her feel more "the part" as she gathered with the others in the kitchen, where everyone made themselves mugs of coffee or herbal tea before settling down for the meeting. Before coming downstairs, she'd popped her head round Su Linn's door, somehow guessing the girl might need encouragement to join in. Judging by Su Linn's look of relief, she'd done the right thing.

Molly, on the other hand, didn't seem her usual confident self.

"Do you think there will be trouble about the cupboard falling off? We won't be blamed for overloading it, will we?"

"I doubt it," Tony replied. "I've been here for over a year now, and the landlady's always been pretty reasonable."

Hans didn't look so sure.

"Remember, it is her son we shall be seeing this evening. He may not be so understanding."

Growing Pains

I LOVE to visit gardens
Where everything is bright,
The lawns are always neatly edged,
There's not a weed in sight!

Tall flowers are staked, the pruning's done,
There's beauty everywhere,
The scent of rose and heliotrope
Pervades the evening air.

My own, by way of contrast,
Is such a sorry sight –
The roses full of greenfly,
The asters mildew white.

The tubs are dry, that plant has died,
The lawn could do with mowing.
I need to prune, replant and feed
To try to keep things growing.

I'd like to blame the aspect, soil,
The weather's icy blast,
But none of these must matter, as
The weeds grow very fast!

– Eliza Barret.

The silence that followed this remark was broken by the shrill tring of the doorbell, making them all jump.

"It looks as if we're about to find out." Tony stood up.

Theresa wasn't sure what she expected when Tony led the newcomer into the room. Someone big and burly, perhaps, who had no truck with students and would expect them to pay for the damage. Instead, a pleasant-looking, fair-haired man in his mid to late twenties walked in, wearing a suit and tie.

"Hi." He smiled warmly as he shook hands with each of them in turn. "I'm Gavin. Sorry, Mum's not around at the moment. She's visiting my aunt Trudy over in Norfolk. You're going to have to make do with me, I'm afraid."

He nodded understandingly as they explained what had happened, and had a good look at the section of wall in question, complete with holes.

"It looks like there wasn't much in the way of support. Mum only bought the house three years ago. The kitchen was still fairly new, so she left that alone, although she had the rest of the house redecorated. These cupboards aren't designed to take much weight, but I've been a student myself, so I know what it's like to share a kitchen with several other people and have to fit stuff in where you can."

He took a tape measure out of his jacket pocket and measured up where the cupboard had been, writing down the figures in a notebook.

"It's a standard size. I'll pick up a replacement at the builders' merchants off the ring road on Saturday and fit it myself. I'll also put some extra supports underneath so the same thing won't happen again."

"Where did you go to university?" Tony asked as he handed him a mug of coffee.

"Not far from your neck of the woods, if I've placed your accent correctly," Gavin replied. "I had a whale of a time. I got to know all sorts of people I'd never have come across otherwise. That's one of the great things about being a student, as I imagine you've already found out for yourselves by now. Are you all settling in well?"

An awkward silence hovered over the group. Theresa cleared her throat.

"It can be a little difficult sometimes. This is a lovely house, but it's a bit of a walk from campus, which makes it quite awkward to go to social events in the evening."

To her surprise, Su Linn and Molly both nodded enthusiastically.

"I see your point," Gavin agreed. "But surely one of the advantages of renting a big house like this means a few of you can go out together? And if you're staying in, this social area's useful, with the armchairs and big coffee table. So often you hear of housemates just sitting in their own rooms instead of enjoying each other's company. Hopefully that's not the case here." He paused. "Or is it?"

"It is early days," Hans said after a moment. "Everyone's been busy finding where their feet have gone. I'm sure that will change soon. And, ladies," he added, with a smile that made his eyes crinkle, "if any of you are worried about getting to or coming back from events, just tell me and I'll walk with you. All you have to do is text me. It will be no problem."

Apart from the odd hiccup with the idiom, his English was very good, Theresa realised. His remarks belied the slightly aloof impression that she had had of Hans so far. Then again, she'd hardly seen enough of him – or the others – to judge fairly.

"Or me," Tony offered. "In fact, I think we should all exchange numbers so there's always someone to contact, even just to meet up for a coffee."

"That's the spirit." Gavin put his empty mug down. "Thanks for the drink, guys. I'd better go. My girlfriend's cooking dinner for me tonight, and I'll be in big trouble if it gets burned because I'm late. I'll sort out the cupboard over the weekend. While I'm at it, I'll pick up a cheap dinner service. It won't be anything fancy, but at least you'll all have enough plates to eat off. You seem a nice bunch. I hope you enjoy living here."

W HAT an eventful couple of days!" Theresa's mother commented when she'd told her about it and they'd both finished laughing. "I'll say," Theresa agreed. "I feel so much happier now."
After Gavin had gone, the five of them had spent the rest of the evening round the table, telling each other a bit about themselves before moving on to discuss all sorts of subjects, including the possibility of setting up a cooking rota so they could all eat together. Molly was, in fact, studying chemistry, and her self-assurance turned out to be a front. Su Linn started coming out of her shell, and Tony and Hans both kept reducing everyone to tears of laughter.

"I must admit that's a relief," her mum said now. "You may have pretended everything was fine before, but I could tell you weren't really settling. You should work hard, of course, but you should also be enjoying yourself." She paused. "To be honest, it's felt very strange here with both you and your brother gone. Even the cat's still looking for you!"

"Aw. Make sure you stroke Monty for me."

"Don't worry. He's getting plenty of attention. What you've just told me has made me think, though. I've been telling you not to stay sitting in your room, when all that time that's what your father and I have been doing, in our living-room. It's so easy to find yourself slipping into these patterns without noticing."

For a fleeting moment, Theresa felt as if their roles had been reversed.

"You should get out more, Mum."

"You're right. The trouble is, we're a bit out of the way here."

"It's not as though you need to get someone to walk you back. Anyway, isn't there a quiz at the pub in the village tomorrow night? They usually have one on Thursdays. There are some good films on at the cinema, too. It wouldn't take you long to get there in the car."

Theresa smiled. Hans, true to his word, would be walking her back tomorrow night. Not only that, but he'd be with her for most of the evening, as they'd arranged to go to the cinema.

"It will make a refreshing change from the library," he'd joked, not aloof after all. Just shy – and unsure how to ask her out.

As Theresa set her alarm for the next morning, she reminded herself that she must call for Molly and Su Linn, as they all had lectures at the same time and had arranged to walk in together.

She laid her head on her pillow with a truly contented sigh for the first time since coming here. It looked as though her life was finally going to turn out well after all, and hopefully without any cupboards falling off any more walls. ■

I'd Like To Know....

Sit back and enjoy this classic selection of vintage queries from the lovely readers of the "Friend"!

Q **DOES** anyone else remember "Potato Pete" and "Doctor Carrot"? They used to have their own songs and slogans during World War II. I think someone famous sang one of their songs. Can you help?

– Mrs W.P., Newbury.

A **THE** Ministry of Agriculture launched one of the best-known slogans ever just one month after the declaration of war in 1939 – Dig For Victory. Essential crops were needed for families at home and to free up space on merchant shipping convoys. Home-grown carrots were in plentiful supply and "Doctor Carrot" was introduced to try to get people to eat them in different ways (curried carrot and carrot jam were two suggestions). "Potato Pete" had his own song, vocals by the late Betty Driver (Betty Williams in "Coronation Street"), and a recipe book. By 1943, over a million tons of vegetables were being grown in gardens and allotments.

. . . .

Q **I HAVE** always been the proud owner of a teapot and tea cosy – as was my mother before me and my grandmother before her. I can't tell you how disappointed I am that none of my children own either. They use coffee granules or say that they just drop a tea bag in a mug and don't need a tea pot or cosy. Can you tell me when the tradition of teapots and cosies started? Perhaps that will make me feel a bit better!

– Mrs O.F., Barnsley.

A **TEA** cosies are traditionally made of cloth or wool and are used to insulate the teapot and keep the tea warm. The first documented use of a tea cosy in Britain was in 1867 and it was probably used by the Duchess of Bedford as she was the one who established the activity of afternoon tea. Afternoon tea was a time to catch up on gossip and chat, so a tea cosy was used to keep the tea in the pot warm while the aristocratic ladies kept up to date with all the news. Although your family may not use teapots and cosies, Mrs F., rest assured that they both remain very popular and tea connoisseurs insist that tea made in a teapot tastes better!

Illustration by Mark Viney.

The Wandering Minstrel

by Lydia Jones.

YOU can come out now, maid. I know you have been listening."
Millie's heart began to batter against her ribs, and beneath her
linen bonnet her skin prickled in terror.

She hadn't meant to stop. She'd been returning from market
with the day's dinner ingredients for Cook when the beautiful
music had made her set down her basket and hide amongst the trees.

Between leaves she'd peeped at the dark-haired young man sitting in
roadside dust, his broad shoulders hunched over the strange-looking

123

instrument, his eyes staring trance-like into the distance. For a few moments she'd allowed herself to be transported by the rich, melodious sound, but now she had been spotted.

"Come, woman – show yourself. What mean you by peering at a man so strangely?"

"Please, sir, I meant no ill."

Her legs trembled so, she wasn't sure she could trust them.

"Come forward and see what it is you watch so secretly."

His tone was gentle – not the rough speech of a man of the road.

She set her basket in the dust before him, concentrating on the cabbages inside.

"Lift your head, maid. Am I not to see your face when you have been staring at mine this half hour past?"

"Indeed I have not, sir!"

Eyes a deeper blue than Millie had ever seen were laughing at her.

"That's better."

His smile was warm. It made her brave enough to speak up.

"Please, sir, what manner of instrument is it you play?"

"This?" He stroked the instrument's curves as if it were a live thing. "It is my pride; my heart's greatest joy. 'Tis a hurdy-gurdy."

"I thought so." Her tone was full of wonder. "'Tis an instrument of Queen Elizabeth's court, is it not?"

"Usually, aye."

The blue eyes flashed anger and what might have been sorrow, but the expression passed in an instant to be replaced with the warm smile.

"But this one is all mine. We roam the world together."

"Roam?"

Millie's insides squeezed as she remembered her situation – speaking to a stranger on the open road.

"I am with the Michaelmas Fair," he replied.

"The fair?"

The man laughed heartily.

"Have you become a caged bird that echoes my words to me?" Once more his eyes sparkled with mirth.

"Indeed, I have taken enough of your time. I must return with my provisions."

"A safe journey, then, to you and your cabbages." His laughing voice pursued her. "Perhaps our paths will cross again."

Millie flushed. It would certainly not be proper, but a tiny part of her couldn't help but hope it might be so.

* * * *

"Millie, where have you been?"

Cook clattered knives on to a chopping board.

"A fine assistant cook you are, to take such an age finding me what is needed from market. Though why Sir Gerald cannot content himself with the victuals grown in his own garden, but must hanker after strange vegetables, I cannot tell. The gardeners here grow only the best."

Knowing the head gardener to be Cook's husband, Millie made no comment.

"It is all to do with trying to outshine Lord Heysham, that's what it is. A fine state of affairs: a gentleman for ever wanting to be better than his neighbours."

Millie began work on the vegetables.

"And now he tells me . . ." Cook slammed the iron door of the brick oven ". . . we are to have a banquet, if you please. A feast on the day of the fair. To celebrate, he says, the first birthday of his son and the bringing in of the harvest together. There'll be no time off for anyone in this kitchen for the next few days, so don't expect it."

"But we get a half day for the fair." The kitchen maid stopped salt-scrubbing dishes. "'Tis tradition."

"I know, Ruby, but perhaps it is for the best. Though there are wonders to see, a fair is not a place for respectable people to linger. 'Tis fine for Sir Gerald and his lady, but poor folk are likely to fall prey to thieves and vagabonds in such a place. Fair folk are not to be trusted."

Thinking of the dark-haired musician with the laughing eyes, Millie's stomach twisted.

"They're not all bad, surely?"

"They're little more than common vagrants," Cook insisted. "And we all know how Her Majesty's law deals with them."

Her fingers twisted the neck of a fowl.

Millie scraped vegetables into the pottage pot, glad of the fire's heat to excuse her burning cheeks.

"There was a maid over at Heysham Hall whose reputation was ruined by a man from the fair," Jane, the housemaid, said as she sat beside Millie's bed later.

"How?"

"She merely went walking with him, but she was ruined just the same. No respectable working man would look at a girl who held herself so cheaply as to consort with fair folk."

Millie pulled her chemise more tightly around herself and snuffed the tallow candle. She included in her prayers a fervent request that no-one should have been witness to her conversation with the fair musician that day.

*   *   *   *

In preparation for the feast Millie was sent to market most days. Each time she passed the fair's common the tents seemed to have increased. Once she glimpsed a man walking on two tall wooden poles, and another day one who seemed to be throwing and catching several coloured balls all at the same time.

Though she kept her head down and didn't stop, her treacherous heart couldn't help hoping for sight of the softly spoken musician, but she never saw him again until the day of her greatest peril.

She heard the roaring as she rounded the bend in the road that day. In the second it took to wonder at the source, Millie stepped into mortal danger.

Blocking her path was the largest creature she had ever seen – bigger than a horse and covered in brown fur. Standing on its hindquarters the beast stared at Millie with enraged black eyes, its mouth revealing monstrous teeth and its forepaws flailing in the air.

She couldn't move; she couldn't breathe.

"Stay!"

Suddenly the young musician was between Millie and the beast.

"He will calm to music but you must stay still."

Millie could only nod as the man stepped forward and began to play his flute.

After a few seconds the roaring ceased. The creature tipped its head to one side and emitted a small whining sound. Then, to Millie's astonishment, it began to dance, its huge paws lifting and falling in time to music.

It was the most wondrous thing – the savage beast that mere seconds before had seemed to threaten her life, now dancing meekly in time to the flute's tune.

There was shouting and a crowd of men appeared with ropes, then the creature was led back to the fair's site.

Only then did Millie begin to tremble and, as she fell, a pair of strong arms encircled her.

"Mistress Cabbage." The young musician smiled. "If we are to keep meeting on the road in this way, I think I might know your name."

"Millie," she said, acutely conscious of his embrace, but still too weak to move. "Millie Weaver."

"Millie Weaver," he repeated in the gentle tone she remembered so well. "Well, Mistress Weaver, my name is Roger De Clancy, and it appears I am entirely at your service."

His deep blue eyes were mesmerising.

"What creature was that, sir?"

"'Twas the fair's dancing bear. The poor creature has been taught from a cub to perform to music. It is the only thing that stills him. In that he and I are alike: we both have music in our souls."

"You saved my life. I cannot thank you enough."

Millie made an attempt to recover, removing herself from his arms, but her heart banged so hard it hurt.

"Perhaps I did. Perhaps not." He looked sad. "But you need not be afraid that I will claim a debt. I hope perhaps that we might meet again. But I remain your

Believe In Yourself

BELIEVE in yourself, in whatever you do,
Your courage, your efforts will carry you through.
Believe you can do things, just try, do your best,
You'll find that in life you've been put to the test.
One day you'll succeed – if your aim's meant to be,
Your positive thoughts will from doubt set you free.
Don't worry if your path's not easy to tread,
Hold on to your dreams and go forging ahead.

Whatever is right then one day you'll receive,
Depending on if in yourself you believe;
If you change direction and divert your aim,
When your path feels good and your motive's the same,
Your instinct's enough, so just follow your star –
Though maybe your life is just right where you are.
Keep faith, be content if your progress seems slow,
You'll get there one day if you go with the flow.

– Chrissy Greenslade.

servant, Mistress Weaver."

And then, with a most gentlemanly bow, he was gone.

W E are all to go to the fair, after all."
Ruby, the kitchen maid, danced around Millie while Cook relieved her of her basket.

"'Tis true. It seems her ladyship is again with child and Sir Gerald is so delighted he has said we are all to accompany them to the fair and the banquet be put off till the following day."

Everyone was buzzing with excitement at the anticipated treat. Millie told no-one of her own adventure, but at night she lay awake, replaying events in her mind, remembering the feel of Roger De Clancy's arms.

∗　∗　∗　∗

The servants stayed together as they had been warned to do. The smell of hog roast filled their nostrils as they marvelled at a man eating fire and a team of acrobats able to walk on hands and build a pyramid of their bodies. Dressed in finery for the occasion, Millie's bear danced, but it was not Roger playing the flute. In spite of the distractions Millie felt a pang of disappointment.

All at once the haunting melody that had halted her on the road came to her.

A crowd had gathered. Roger was seated on a low wooden chair, coaxing such beautiful music from his hurdy-gurdy that everyone watched in silent

Thinkstockphotos.

127

reverence. Millie noticed again how far away was his gaze and wondered at what sadness lay beneath the surface.

When the music stopped everyone cheered and clapped. As Roger acknowledged them his gaze found Millie and the grin gave light to all his features. With an imperceptible nod which she knew was just for her, Roger this time took up a lyre.

Recitals on the flute and fiddle followed as well as more music from the hurdy-gurdy, till it seemed everyone at the fair must be there.

"You!" Sir Gerald's voice boomed above the assembled crowd. "What is your name?"

"Roger De Clancy, sir."

"You are not a labouring man, I think. How come you to play so well?"

"I was taught by the best. I am the third son of a gentleman. My father wanted me for the law but I would not give up my music. When I would not defer to his wishes I was cast out with only my instruments to sustain me."

Little whispered gasps rippled round the crowd.

"So you are a travelling minstrel?" Sir Gerald sounded shocked.

"A man must eat, sir, however great his love of music."

"And the travelling life suits you well?"

"In truth I am tired of it, but I will not abandon the very essence of myself."

"So, then, Roger De Clancy . . ." Sir Gerald strode forward. "If I were to offer you a position in my household, you might consider?"

Did Roger's gaze seek out hers in the crowd? Millie wasn't sure she was still breathing.

"My wife and I entertain greatly; we have need of excellent music. And I would have my daughters taught by a master such as yourself. Come, sir, what do you say? Do we have an agreement?"

Sir Gerald offered Roger his hand. As Millie watched, Roger's face broke into his beautiful smile and he reached out to accept the proffered handshake. Then, in a gesture that set her insides buzzing like a swarm of bees, he stared right at her, smiled and bowed.

"You can come to the house tomorrow to settle terms," Sir Gerald told him.

"I'll wager that's something with which Lord Heysham can't compete," Sir Gerald whispered, taking his lady by the arm. "A musician and tutor of his own – and a man who plays with such distinction.

"Come, my dear," he said aloud. "Let us hasten home. We have much to celebrate: our estate prospers and our son is strong and healthy. Truly the future is set fair for us."

Perhaps for me, too, Millie thought, casting a last shy smile at the dark-haired musician with the laughing eyes.

In fact, her future looked to be set fairer than at any time she could remember. ■

Leek, Staffordshire

KNOWN locally as "the Queen of the moorlands", Leek in Staffordshire is a pretty market town on the edge of the Peak District. The River Churnet flows close by, though the town itself is built on the slopes and the top of a hill. The steep streets around the market square house a variety of interesting buildings and shops, including many independent retailers.

Once the home of a large cattle market, reflecting the agricultural past of the surrounding area, Leek itself was known for its silk weaving and was for a time the home of William Morris, the Victorian designer whose famous patterns are still admired and in use today for furnishing fabrics and wallpaper.

Many of Leek's Victorian textile mills remain, though have mostly been adapted to other purposes, including antiques centres and art galleries. ■

No Girls Allowed!

by Alice Renaud.

CHARLIE pulled up his cassock and jumped over a pumpkin. "Hurry up, Jenny! I've time for one game of conkers before lunch!"

Jenny didn't move. She sat on the chancel step, surrounded by fruit and vegetables, staring wistfully at the empty choir stalls.

Charlie pushed a marrow out of the way and sat next to her.

"Did you enjoy the service?"

"Oh, yes! I love the Harvest Festival. And you sang so well.''

Charlie twisted his surplice between his fingers.

"I'll never sing as well as you. It's not fair you can't join the choir just 'cause you're a girl."

Jenny shrugged.

"It's a boys' choir. I'll just have to get over it and stop moping."

Charlie didn't know what to say, so he looked at the people who were filing out of the church. Mr Turvey, the choirmaster, walked past clutching his music sheets.

"Have you tried talking to him?" Charlie nodded in his direction.

She shook her head.

"There's no point – he'd say no. The choir in this church has never accepted girls." She got to her feet. "Come on! Do you want to get beaten at conkers, or not?"

✳   ✳   ✳   ✳

As Charlie made his way to the church for Evensong later that afternoon, he thought about Jenny. Boys' choirs didn't take girls, even ones with only 10 boys in them. Yet perhaps it was time for a change.

He reached the churchyard with 20 minutes to spare and stood a while under the horse chestnut tree. Conkers gleamed among the fallen leaves. He collected a few, but his heart wasn't in it. If only Jenny could join the choir. Singing was all she'd ever wanted to do since she was small.

The door of the church creaked open and the vicar came out.

"Hello, Charlie! You're early."

Illustration by Pat Gregory.

Charlie liked Father Paul. When he smiled, his whole face creased up and, unlike some other grown-ups, he always had time to talk to you. Especially when you had a problem.

"Found any good ones?" The priest pointed at the glossy conkers in Charlie's hand.

"I wasn't really looking," he admitted. "Father, what would you do if you wanted to join a club, but they didn't want you?"

The vicar looked at him seriously.

"Funny you should ask that. I was once in that situation. Before I became a vicar I was a banker. When I decided to change my life and train for the priesthood, many people thought it a bad idea. They were convinced I wasn't cut out for it."

Charlie stared.

"How did you get them to change their minds?"

Father Paul rubbed his chin thoughtfully.

"Well, Charlie, once people see what you have to offer, and that you're really committed to doing your best, they'll welcome you."

Charlie pondered this a moment.

"You have to show them what you can do and then they'll accept you, even if you're different?"

"That's right. Does that help?"

Charlie beamed at him.

"Yes! Thanks, Father!"

He ran into the church, wanting to catch the choirmaster before the other choirboys arrived. If the vicar was right, Jenny might be able to achieve her dream after all.

Mr Turvey was standing by the organ, staring at a music sheet. Charlie took a deep breath.

"Mr Turvey, I have a friend who'd love to join the choir."

The choirmaster's face lit up.

"Does he have a good voice?"

Charlie looked down.

"Er, he's a she."

Mr Turvey sighed.

"I can't have a girl in the choir, Charlie. Not yet. Maybe one day, but this is a very traditional parish."

"I know," Charlie replied. "But maybe she could study with us?"

"Study?"

Charlie nodded.

"She loves singing, and she wants to learn to do it properly. If she could just join us for choir practice, you could teach her how to read music, and she could sing with us. She loves church music."

Mr Turvey's mouth lifted a bit at the corner.

"She does? Classically minded, then?"

Charlie wasn't sure how classic Jenny's mind was, but he nodded.

The choirmaster smiled.

"All right, I'm convinced. Bring your friend tomorrow, and we'll see how she gets on."

IT'LL be all right," Charlie whispered as he led Jenny into the vestry. Nine heads turned and nine pairs of eyes stared at them. Especially at Jenny. "Boys, this is Jenny," Mr Turvey said. "She's joining us as an honorary music student and will practise with us. I know you'll make her feel very welcome. We'll start with a psalm."

Soon the choristers were too busy concentrating on their singing to worry about the new arrival and Jenny relaxed. Charlie's heart lifted when her voice joined the choir, just a little bit purer and higher than anybody else's.

"Good, Jenny," the choirmaster said.

She beamed. Charlie smiled to himself. Before too long, his best friend would join the choir for good, he was sure.

* * * *

Bang! Charlie's conker exploded into pieces. Jenny let out a cry of triumph.

"I've won again!"

Charlie nodded and tossed away the remaining fragments.

Jenny frowned.

"Are you all right? You've been really quiet today."

Charlie dug his hands into his pockets.

"Jen, it's been a year since you started practising with us."

Jenny examined her conker for signs of damage.

"Yep! It's been the best year ever."

Charlie eyed her doubtfully.

"Even though you still haven't joined the choir?"

Understanding dawned on her face.

"Is that what's bothering you? But you didn't think they'd let me become a chorister just because I study with you, did you?"

Charlie kicked at the yellowing leaves around his feet.

"I thought if they saw how good you are and how hard you work, they'd change their minds."

Jenny hugged him.

"Charlie, it's sweet of you, but don't be sad for me. I love singing with you all and I'm learning so much. Mr Turvey's a brilliant teacher. Come on, we're going to be late for Evensong."

In spite of Jenny's cheeriness, Charlie had trouble concentrating during the service. Would his friend's voice ever be heard here, in the candlelit nave, where it belonged? It didn't seem likely. Then Father Paul made an announcement that deepened Charlie's gloom. He'd been promoted to archdeacon, and would be leaving them at the end of the month!

Charlie really liked Father Paul. Perhaps the new vicar would be completely against girl singers, and then Jenny would never get a chance to join the choir!

THE following weeks whizzed by in a whirl of rehearsals. The bishop was coming to the church on All Saints' Day, to install the new vicar, and Mr Turvey was determined that his choir would shine.

"This anthem," he declared one day, waving a music sheet at them, "is His Grace's favourite. Unfortunately it's also quite tricky, especially the solo part. So we all need to work hard!"

And they did. Especially Jenny, even though she wouldn't be singing with them. One evening she even stayed late, after the others had left, to help Charlie practise the anthem.

Halfway through the first stanza a knock at the door interrupted them. Charlie opened it and a young, dark-haired woman beamed at him.

"Hello! I see I'm too late. Mr Turvey has already left, hasn't he?"

"Yes. He's gone to the vicarage to talk with Father Paul." Charlie pointed towards the large Victorian house on the other side of the road. "You can still catch him if you hurry."

Then curiosity made him ask, "Are you the mum of someone who wants to join the choir?"

The woman laughed. She pushed her scarf away from her neck, revealing a dog collar.

"No, I'm actually your new vicar. My name's Kate."

She extended her hand and Charlie shook it, dazed. He'd never met a lady priest before.

"Perhaps the parish is changing after all," Jenny said after Reverend Kate had left. "If they accept a female vicar, who knows what will happen next?"

✷   ✷   ✷   ✷

"A disaster!" Mr Turvey groaned.

All the choristers and Jenny looked at their shoes. All Saints' Day had arrived and Tom, the lead singer, had come down with a cold. His throat was sore and he couldn't sing a note, let alone the solo part of the anthem.

Mr Turvey sighed and riffled through his papers.

"We'll just have to skip the anthem. Sorry, boys, none of you can sing the solo well enough."

"Jenny can." The words came out of Charlie's mouth before his brain could stop them. Everyone stared at him as he glanced anxiously at Mr Turvey. Was he going to get angry, or laugh?

But the choirmaster just rubbed his chin and stared at Jenny.

"Can you try to sing the solo part?" he asked. "For me?"

"*Panis angelicus, fit panis hominum . . .*"

Charlie felt tears sting his eyes as Jenny's voice soared, so beautiful it made your heart ache. When she finished, Mr Turvey took off his glasses and polished them on his handkerchief.

"It would be a shame to let all that hard work go to waste," he muttered. "We have to move with the times, especially now we have a lady vicar. Some won't like it, but it's worth ruffling a few feathers to keep the choir alive."

Charlie wasn't sure which church members had feathers, but his heart was racing with hope and excitement. As for Jenny, she looked as though she'd stop breathing any minute.

Mr Turvey put his glasses back on his nose.

"Well, young Jenny, we'd better get you robed."

He opened a cupboard and presented her with a cassock and a surplice. Jenny struggled into the unfamiliar robes.

"But what will people think?" she fretted.

"They'll think you're brilliant as soon as you start singing!" Charlie said.

Mr Turvey chuckled.

"Charlie's right. Now, look at yourself."

They gazed at the tall mirror on the wall, which reflected Jenny in her bright red cassock and immaculate white surplice, with the wide sleeves falling from her arms like the wings of a bird.

"You look like an angel!" Charlie said.

The choirmaster nodded.

"So she should. In a church, the choir are meant to represent the angels singing in Heaven. That's why your surplices have such wide sleeves, to imitate wings."

"And angels don't have to be boys, they can be girls!" Charlie pointed out.

He felt great. This was going to be the best service ever, because his best friend would be singing next to him. But when he turned round after the rehearsal, Jenny was gone.

Fear gripped Charlie's heart. The sung Mass would start in a few minutes. He had to find her!

HE discovered her under the bare branches of the horse chestnut tree, chewing her fingernails.

"I don't know if I can do it, Charlie." Jenny's voice shook.

He put an arm around her shoulders.

"Of course you can. You must have rehearsed this anthem hundreds of times!"

Jenny stared at the dead leaves at her feet. The long sleeves of her surplice billowed in the cold, damp wind.

"I wish Mr Turvey hadn't given me the solo part. I've never sung before the congregation, and today the bishop's here! What if they don't like me?"

Charlie racked his brain for reassuring words. What would Father Paul say?

"Don't think about them. Sing for Mr Turvey, for me, and the others in the choir."

He pointed at the large crucifix above the church door.

"Sing for Him! He doesn't care if you're a girl or a boy. I don't think He even cares how well you sing, as long as you do your best."

Jenny pondered this for a moment. Then she smiled.

"You're right. Thanks for being so patient with me, Charlie. I'm so lucky to be in the choir, and I'm even luckier to have a friend like you! Let's go and sing!"

Hand in hand, they walked back towards the church, and soon their voices rose towards the clouds, mingled with those of the whole congregation.

"Angel voices, ever singing, round thy throne of light . . ." ■

I'd Like To Know....

Sit back and enjoy this classic selection of vintage queries from the lovely readers of the "Friend"!

Q **I READ** somewhere about Tyrone Power being in the military during World War II. Did he serve and what exactly did he do? He was so handsome and my favourite film star!

– *Mrs A.P., Wiltshire.*

A **AMERICAN** film star Tyrone Power (1914–58) enlisted in the Marine Corps in August 1942. He attended boot camp, but because he had already logged 180 solo hours as a pilot prior to enlisting, he was able to undergo a short intensive flight training course and earn his wings. He flew cargo in and wounded Marines out during the Battles of Iwo Jima and Okinawa. He was released from active duty in January 1946 as a First Lieutenant.

. . . .

Q **MY** job as a young child used to be to sprinkle the cold tea leaves from the teapot on to my mother's plants in the garden. She was convinced they helped her plants to grow and I liked to think I was helping. This got me to thinking about tea leaves and tea bags, however. When did tea bags become popular in the UK? Can you help?

– *Mrs L.S., Manchester.*

A **MATERIAL** shortages during World War II slowed the mass adoption of tea bags in Britain, and it was not until the 1950s that they really took off. Tea bags gained quickly in popularity because you did not need to empty out the used tea leaves from the teapot. Tetley was the company who introduced tea bags to Britain in 1953 and by the early 1960s tea bags made up 3% of the tea buying market. By 2007, however, tea bags made up a phenomenal 96% of the British market!

Illustration by Jim Dewar/Thinkstockphotos.

If Wishes Were Horses...

by Jenny Roman.

HILARY gazed through the kitchen window at the paddock beyond the garden, and her heart turned over. Her small bay pony stood forlornly by the fence, whinnying plaintively. "Oh, Bramble!" Hilary fought the lump in her throat.

It had been three weeks since they'd lost Jasper, Bramble's companion for the last 19 years, and the remaining pony was clearly not enjoying his solitary existence. At first, Hilary had hoped that poor old Bramble would adjust, but as the days went by, and the normally happy pony continued to stand by the fence, whinnying for his lost friend, it was becoming obvious she would need to take action. A new companion was required.

137

Hilary was surprised to find the thought quite daunting. It was silly really. She'd had horses all her life. The children had all been through the horsey phase, so in the old days there had been a succession of ponies coming and going. A string of faded rosettes hung along the wall, and the cabinet in the dining-room was crammed with trophies.

It didn't bear thinking about that in the not-too-distant future, the kitchen window would overlook an empty paddock, but Bramble himself was in his twenties now, and poor old Jasper had been even older. She had to face facts – she herself wasn't getting any younger. Should she find a new home for Bramble?

The thought brought tears to her eyes. No, not while he was still fit and healthy. Hilary took a carrot from the vegetable basket under the worktop, pushed open the back door, and picked her way across the grass to the fence. Bramble's ears pitched forward at the sight of her, and he let out another piercing whinny.

"You need a new friend, don't you, little chap?" she said, scratching him behind the ears while he nibbled the carrot. There were grey hairs around his eyes and in the tufty hair of his bushy mane. But his coat was rich and shiny, and his eyes were bright. "I promise, Bramble, to find you a new friend so you can live out your days in contented company."

Hilary left him to finish his carrot with a thoughtful expression on his face, and went back into the house. She tried to push away the thought that it wasn't just Bramble who was feeling lonely. No, she wasn't lonely exactly. Unlike Bramble, she was quite content in her own company, most of the time. The loss of her husband Jack, nine years earlier, had settled into a dull ache. The children, long flown the nest, were great, popping in when they could, but it wasn't the same as having people around on a regular basis.

Around her, the house waited silently for some action from her. The clock in the hall ticked off the moments of her indecision.

In the paddock, Bramble let out another pitiful whinny and her heart contracted.

"Come on!" she told herself. She snatched up her car keys and handbag, and headed out of the door.

THE equine section of the local paper yielded nothing of any interest, but the noticeboard in the feed merchants was awash with adverts. Hilary had taken down the details of three possible new friends for Bramble. The first had been an aged Shetland, who had initially sounded perfect, but turned out to be even older than the advert had suggested. When the owners had listed all his various ailments, Hilary decided it might be unwise to take him on. She had visions of huge vet bills, followed by lots more heartache, and a search for another replacement companion pony a few months down the line.

The next visit was to see five ponies who needed rehoming. The wording had made it sound as though the place was a rescue centre, but it turned out to be a private ad. Hilary stood by the solid-looking bungalow and watched the ponies – all two-year-olds – careering around a large field, nipping and chasing each other. She made her decision in seconds. Poor old Bramble was too old for such antics.

"You'd have your pick, like." The owner was a well-weathered man in his fifties, wearing aged boots and a fleece, the original colour of which was difficult to judge. He wouldn't quite meet Hilary's eye, but seemed to keep her in his peripheral vision. "Or I could let you have the lot for the price of four."

How much fun she'd have had in her youth, bringing on five youngsters! But that thought now filled her with horror. It was obvious that taking even one home would be a grave mistake. She'd known that from the moment she'd set eyes on them.

Apologising for wasting the gentleman's time, she made her way back to the car. On the passenger seat was her notepad. Just one more to go. A child's riding pony seeking a quiet life; home more important than price. Hilary typed the postcode into her satnav and set off.

The address was a neat brick house on an estate, where the door was answered by an anxious-looking woman in her forties, and her pretty daughter, eyes red from crying.

Hilary introduced herself, and said she'd come about the pony.

"I'm Alison," the woman said, "and this is Lottie." She put an arm around the girl's shoulders.

"Is it your pony?" Hilary asked the girl gently.

Lotte nodded, blinking furiously.

"His name's Oscar."

"He's kept at a yard just up the road," Alison explained. "It's a few minutes in the car."

They piled into Alison's car, and Hilary smiled to herself at the familiarity of hay in the foot wells, and the jumble of coats and wellies in the boot.

Lottie sat in the back, and when Hilary glanced round, the girl was staring resolutely out of the window. Hilary felt for her. It was horrible growing out of a pony and having to sell it on. It was like selling your best friend.

The yard was a tumble-down side-line to a farm. To the right were the stables, and to the left was a large field, sloping down to some woodland in the distance. Half a dozen horses and ponies stood around the gate waiting to be brought in, while even more were dotted around the field, picking at the sparse grazing.

"There's Oscar," Lottie said, leaning forward between the front seats and pointing. "The grey."

Hilary was surprised. Oscar was bigger than he'd seemed in the photos. Easily big enough for this slip of a girl. So Lottie had not outgrown him then.

They climbed out of the car, and Lottie went to catch Oscar, shooing the other ponies away from the gate. She brought him into the yard so Hilary could give him a proper look over.

"We should have brought him in earlier and cleaned him up a bit," Alison said ruefully.

"Oh, it's no problem," Hilary said, rubbing Oscar's neck, and letting him give her a good sniff. "I'm quite happy to see them in the rough."

"We like to keep him out as much as possible," Alison replied. "It's more natural for him than being stuck in the stable."

"But he gets bullied," Lottie added, stroking his nose gently. "He's too much of a softy to stand up for himself."

Oscar regarded Hilary with calm, brown eyes and she felt his warm breath against her hands. He was a lovely pony.

"How old did you say he was?"

"He's sixteen," Lottie replied.

"And he's sound and healthy?"

"Oh, yes." Alison nodded. "Never been lame in all the time we've had him, and he's never had to see the vet except for routine jabs."

Hilary looked sideways at her.

"Why are you selling him?"

Alison sighed.

"Lottie's dad got made redundant last year, and he's found something else, but on a much smaller salary. We're only just covering the mortgage. We've tried for Lottie's sake to hold on, but they've just put the rent up here, and we can't afford it."

"And there's nowhere cheaper for you to keep him?"

"We were offered a field to rent, but it's not practical. Here, there's someone to keep an eye on him on weekdays when Lottie's at school and I'm at work. If we just had a field, he'd be stuck on his own most of the time, and we're afraid he'd be scared and hurt himself."

Hilary felt a smile stretch across her face. She gazed at Lottie's tear-stained face.

"I might just have a solution."

D O you think they'll make friends?" Lottie asked.

They had divided Hilary's paddock in two with a length of fence to give the ponies a chance to get to know each other before they went in together. Bramble stood resolutely as close to the fence as he dared, gazing at the new arrival, while Oscar walked round the boundaries of his new

Therapy

THERE are self-help books by the dozen
In case we are feeling depressed.
The bookshops and libraries full to the brim,
Because these days we often feel stressed.
Psychologists, counsellors waiting to help,
Now people are cured by the letter –
CBM, DBT, NLP, CBT –
But I've found that what makes me feel better
Is a hug from a friend, an arm round my shoulders,
A friendly ear listening to me,
A packet of dark chocolate biscuits,
Two cups and a pot of nice tea!

– Eliza Barret.

home. Occasionally, he paused to stretch out his nose timidly towards Bramble, but his nerve would always fail him at the last minute, and he'd wheel away and trot to the other side of the paddock, to begin pacing all over again.

"I'm sure they will," Hilary replied. "It's a big change for both of them. Bramble hasn't lived with any pony other than Jasper for years, and Oscar's used to being in a big group. But they'll settle down. I'll keep an eye on them, don't you worry."

"Thank you," Alison said. The anxiety had left her face, and she smiled warmly at Hilary. "Thank you for all of this. It's perfect."

"It's a pleasure. And don't forget, you're doing me a huge favour, too – giving Bramble a new friend."

"And you're sure you won't mind us coming and going, getting under your feet?" Alison asked.

Hilary shook her head.

"It'll be lovely to see some life about the place again." She turned to Lottie. "And remember, any time you want me to check on him, just let me know."

Lottie had tears in her eyes again. But judging by her smile, this time they were happy tears.

"Thank you!" she cried, and to Hilary's surprise and joy, the little girl threw her arms around her and gave her a big hug.

It took a long time for Hilary to drop off to sleep that night. Despite her assurances that the ponies would be fine, she was alert to each hoof-beat, each snort or shake. Several times, she got up and peeked through her bedroom curtains, trying to make out if Oscar was settling.

When she finally slept, it was a restless night, filled with strange dreams.

The following morning, she woke with a start. It took her a moment to remember why her body felt taught with anxiety, then it came to her. Tumbling out of bed, she threw open the curtains. A chasm of dread opened up inside her. Oscar's side of the paddock was empty.

Then she laughed. The relief flowed through her, making her knees weak, and her breath come in great panting gasps.

The fence was on the ground. In the hazy morning sunshine, Oscar and Bramble were standing together, nose to tail, under the old willow tree. It was a beautiful sight, Oscar's sleek, grey coat contrasting with the cuddly, brown Bramble. She watched Oscar gently nibble the top of Bramble's tail, and in turn, Bramble rubbed his head against Oscar's hocks. They looked like old friends already.

There was the sound of a car in the lane and, a few moments later, Hilary heard the side gate open. Lottie came running into the garden, and across to the paddock fence. She turned and glanced up at Hilary's window and Hilary gave a thumbs-up sign. Lottie grinned and put both of her thumbs up, too.

Hilary pulled on her dressing-gown, listening to Lottie's delighted chatter as she pretended to give the ponies a good telling-off for breaking through the fence.

She went downstairs, put the kettle on, and opened the kitchen window. Alison turned and waved.

"Cup of tea?" Hilary offered through the open window.

"That would be very kind," Alison called back.

Hilary fetched mugs from the cupboard as she heard Lottie calling to the ponies, and Bramble's happy whinny as he saw the hay.

On the wall, the rosette ribbons fluttered in the breeze. Hilary felt her heart fill. It was almost like old times. ▦

Tobermory, Mull

THE little fishing port on the island of Mull in the Inner Hebrides was designed by engineer Thomas Telford in 1788, after the British Fisheries Society recognised the superb natural harbour as an ideal site for a fishing community in the area. The name comes from the Gaelic *Tobar Mhoire*, or Mary's well, after an ancient holy well dedicated to the Virgin Mary in the old settlement.

The town is instantly recognisable with its brightly painted houses fronting the harbour. Many children grew up recognising the harbour front as "Balamory", the fictional Scottish island that was home to beloved characters such as Miss Hoolie, Archie the inventor and PC Plum. The TV favourite was filmed between 2002 and 2005 and continues to be popular with pre-schoolers today.

As well as its role as an active fishing port, the harbour is also the departure point for wildlife and whale-watching cruises, as the seas off the coast are important feeding areas for dolphins, porpoises and basking sharks. ∎

Music Lessons

by Lynne Hallett.

WELL, it certainly needed that." The piano tuner ran his fingers up and down the keys. "Sounds beautiful now, doesn't it?"

"Yes, it does," Grace replied.

"I bet you'll be playing for the rest of the morning once I've gone." He smiled cheerfully at her. He was a jolly man, with a thick mop of white hair and ruddy cheeks.

She shook her head.

"No. It was my husband who played."

"Was? I'm sorry."

"No need," she said brusquely. "It was a while back now."

"Same for me. I just try to keep myself busy, you know? Keeps your mind off things." He turned back to the piano. "Why don't you learn to play?"

"I'm not sure I could at my age."

"You're never too old. Look," he said, fishing in his bag, "here's my card. If you ever change your mind, I could give you a few lessons."

She reached out and took the card. *Ted Johnson*, it said, *Piano Tuner and Teacher*, with all his contact details on it.

"I'll think about it," Grace said, meeting his gaze. His eyes were the colour of chocolate, his expression warm, and for the first time in a long time her heart beat just a little faster.

"I hope you don't think I'm being pushy, but it's a lovely instrument and it deserves to be played."

"Perhaps you're right, Mr Johnson," she said, glancing back at the baby grand as they left the room.

"Oh, Ted, please." He reached out his hand. "It's been a pleasure."

"Likewise." She shook his hand and felt hers disappear within it. He was strong but gentle, rather like Douglas had been.

"Cheerio, then, and maybe I'll be hearing from you." He raised an eyebrow.

"Maybe." She opened the front door. "Goodbye."

Grace smiled as he walked down the path.

Once the door was closed she wandered back into the room which housed the piano, took out a duster and some polish and lovingly cleaned it. She rubbed so hard that she could almost see her face in the surface once she was done. That was how Douglas had always liked it.

For a moment she could almost see him sitting there, moving his fingers

Illustration by David Young.

effortlessly over the keys, swaying in time to the music. On several occasions he had brought tears to her eyes when he played, especially anything by Rachmaninoff. Those pieces always got to her.

But now there was silence. There had been for five years. No-one played the piano any more. She wasn't sure she wanted anyone else to play it. It would be like breaking a spell. New memories would take the place of old ones and she wasn't sure she was ready for that.

HESITANTLY, Grace sat down on the stool and looked at the beautiful ivory keys. Her finger found middle C and she pressed it. The key was heavier than she thought it would be and very cool. The note, however, was rich and resonant. She waited until the sound had disappeared and then closed the lid. Taking a deep breath and exhaling, she pushed the stool back and left the room.

She meandered to the kitchen and took a look at the clock. Was that the time already? Lucy and Sam would be coming over for lunch. There was just enough time to bake a cake before they arrived.

She got out her scales and mixing bowl and set to work making a chocolate sponge. Sam was quite fond of her chocolate cakes and she knew he'd enjoy having a generous slice of this one. It was a shame she didn't get to see them more often, but living at a distance made it difficult for them to visit and school holidays were about the only times they got together. She smiled as she thought of her six-year-old grandson. He was a cute little chap and very bright. He reminded her a lot of Lucy at the same age.

She creamed the butter and sugar together, keeping a steady beat going and folding in the flour and other ingredients at regular intervals. Once the mixture was smooth, she distributed it evenly between two tins and put them into the oven to bake.

While the sponges were cooking, she prepared a chocolate fudge filling, which would serve as the topping as well. Thoughts flitted in and out of her head like butterflies as she mixed and stirred and by the time the doorbell rang, she felt a calm within that she hadn't felt for ages.

"Hi, Mum," Lucy said, giving her a hug and a kiss as she opened the door. "How are you?"

"I'm fine, darling," she said. "And look at you, Sam. I'm sure you've grown again."

He laughed.

"I'll soon be as tall as you, Grandma."

"I dare say you will. How's school?"

"OK. I'm on the top table in Maths and I got a special mention in assembly last week."

"Very good. Now, come through to the kitchen. I have something special for you in there."

"Is it a chocolate cake?" he asked, jumping up and down.

"It might be." Grace smiled.

"I knew you'd make one. Wow!" he said, as he laid eyes on the cake.

"What do you say?" Lucy prompted.

"Thank you, Grandma!"

Soon they were all tucking into the cake.

"It's so yummy," Sam said. "Could I have another piece, please?"

"Of course," Grace replied, cutting him a big slice and putting it on his plate.

"So, how are things really, Mum?" Her daughter looked her right in the eye and for a change she was able to hold the look.

"Better actually."

"That's good." Lucy smiled at her. "It's hard, though, isn't it?"

Grace nodded.

"Yes, but today I saw a glimmer of light at the end of the tunnel. A man came to tune Dad's piano and . . ."

"You have a piano, Grandma? I didn't know that." Sam's blue eyes sparkled.

Grace nodded.

"It was Grandad's piano. It's in a special room next to the front door, but I always keep it closed."

"Why?"

Grace swallowed hard.

146

Dinner Is Served

TONIGHT'S dinner tastes somewhat
  piquant –
Though why, I just cannot be sure.
It's a meal that I've cooked for the family
On many occasions before.

So, what has been added, I wonder?
Some rare or peculiar herb?
A secret ingredient, surely
Has rendered its flavour superb!

Perhaps it's just nicely presented –
Does it seem scrupulously arranged?
No – after a thorough inspection,
I can't see that anything's changed.

But something is definitely different!
Just what have I been overlooking?
I've got it! That's why it's delicious –
It's 'cause someone else did the cooking!

– *Emma Canning.*

"Well, it was Grandad's room and when he died five years ago, there was no-one else to play the piano."

"But there's me now." Sam was bobbing up and down in his seat.

Hurriedly, Lucy spoke up.

"I'm not sure Grandma would want you to play it, Sam. It reminds her of Grandad."

"But I'm learning and I'm very good. Mrs Chambers said so."

Grace frowned.

"You never said he was having lessons, Lucy."

"It was a surprise, Grandma," Sam told her. "So that when you next visited, I could show you what I was doing. But I could show you now, couldn't I?"

Grace looked at Lucy's face, with the furrowed brow, and then at Sam's. His eyes were wide and bright and his cheeks flushed with anticipation.

Grace smiled.

"Well, I think if we get you cleaned up first, then maybe you could play for me, just like Grandad used to. It's a very special piano and you need to have clean fingers to play it."

"OK." He slid out of his chair, pulled up a stool, turned on the tap and washed his hands thoroughly.

"Are you sure about this, Mum?" Lucy asked.

Grace nodded.

"Yes, I am. Your dad would have approved of his grandson playing it."

"I'm finished, Grandma," Sam said, wiping his hands on the towel.

"OK, I'll lead the way and you can show me what you can do."

GRACE led them back up the hallway with its polished floors and opened the door to the piano room.

"Wow!" Sam said. "Look how shiny it is."

"I polished it this morning. Now, what can you play?"

"'Twinkle, Twinkle, Little Star.'"

"My favourite nursery rhyme. Let's get you up here and I'll open the lid for you." Grace got him into position and then sat down in the chair she had always used when Douglas was alive.

"Are you ready?" he asked.

"Yes, we're both ready," she replied. Lucy was sitting in another chair close by.

He started to move his fingers over the keys, tapping out the tune and swinging his legs in time to the music.

"Bravo," Grace said, applauding when he had finished. "Beautiful playing. Encore!"

"What does encore mean, Grandma?" Sam asked, looking at her.

"It means play again."

Sam beamed from ear to ear and set to playing once more. As Grace watched him she could see the odd mannerism which reminded her of Douglas. She wiped a tear from her eye. Making new memories wasn't such a bad thing after all. It didn't replace the old ones; it added to them.

"That was beautiful, darling. Isn't he talented?" She turned to Lucy.

"Just like Dad."

"Yes, just like Dad."

"Can I play again next time I come, Grandma?" Sam piped up.

"Absolutely, Sam."

Once Lucy and Sam had gone, Grace put her hand into her pocket and pulled out the card which the piano tuner had left. She looked at it for a few seconds, then, smiling, she went to the phone and dialled his number.

"Mr Johnson? I mean, Ted. It's Grace Harper here. I've been thinking. Would the offer of some lessons still be open?"

Maybe it was her turn to surprise Lucy and Sam the next time they visited! ■

I'd Like To Know....

Sit back and enjoy this classic selection of vintage queries from the lovely readers of the "Friend"!

Q **MY** family were quite surprised when I told them about the bonfire toffee I used to have as a girl in the early Fifties. My mum regularly made this treat on Guy Fawkes Night and I remember that my brothers and sisters and I couldn't wait. It was a dark toffee that tasted of molasses and it was delicious. The tradition sadly ended with my mum in our family, but I wondered if other readers have heard of this special toffee, too?

– Mrs A.S., Blackburn.

A **BONFIRE** toffee was also known as treacle toffee, cinder toffee, Plot toffee, Tom Trot, claggum (in Scotland) and *loshin du* (in Wales). Bonfire toffee was usually a home-made confectionery and was made from black treacle. It is not really clear why the sweet became associated with Guy Fawkes Night, but it is certain that the toffee was most popular in the north of Britain.

Q **A FRIEND** of mine who lives on the east coast of Scotland often talks about the haar coming in or describes the strange way it rolls up the River Tay. I know she's talking about a fog or mist, but where does the word haar come from?

– Mrs T.E., Lancashire.

A **A HAAR** is a coastal fog typically along lands bordering the North Sea. It is a phrase used mainly in eastern Scotland. Variations on the word include har, hare, harl, harr and hoar and it is thought that the origin may be Saxon.

Q **I WOULD** like to know if John Wayne, the late film star, was ever married. My friend thinks he was married to Maureen O'Hara as they were in a lot of films together. Is she correct?

– Mrs I.S., Grimsby.

A **JOHN WAYNE** starred with Maureen O'Hara in five films between 1948 and 1972, but although they shared on-screen chemistry, they were never married. John Wayne married three times — Josephine Alicia Saenz (1933–1945), Esperanza Baur (1946–1954) and Pilar Pallete (1954 to his death in 1979). He had four children with Josephine and three with Pilar.

Penny For The Guy

by Samantha Tonge.

PENELOPE carried two Tupperware boxes into the Ranger Scout hut. A Penny For The Guy party – whatever next? Nowadays it seemed as if any excuse was used for a celebration. However, she gave a wry smile. It was always fun, seeing her daughter, Georgia, now seventeen, dressed up like an enthusiastic toddler for Hallowe'en. Plus this evening's party was, at least, in support of a good cause. She bit her lip. It was the kind of event she'd have enjoyed chatting over with a partner. That was the hardest thing about being single – not having a special someone on hand to talk to.

"Hello, Mrs Tait," she said now to the Ranger leader who was setting out plastic plates and cups. A sprightly woman, with short auburn-dyed hair, Mrs Tait liked things to be formal but had the heart of Florence Nightingale.

Penelope set down the Tupperware boxes which were full of cupcakes.

"Mrs Jones, it's lovely to see you," the older woman said. "Thank you so much for baking. Home-made fare always goes down well at these charity fund-raisers. Perhaps you could stay and help me price up the rest of the food we're hoping to sell? Unless you are busy, of course."

How could Penelope resist that good-natured smile? She admired Mrs Tait for organising so many events and trips for the girls. Plus – and this was Georgia's favourite – pizza and movie evenings. By the time most teenagers reached Rangers, the mum and dads had become less involved in extra-curricular activities. In fact, many of the young members made their own way there and often the parents rarely saw Mrs Tait.

Penelope lived almost five miles away, so she drove Georgia there in the car.

"How many people do you hope will turn up?" Penelope asked. "The weekend before Bonfire Night is always busy, and there are lots of displays on in the area."

"Well, my three grandchildren can't wait to come and see the competition entries," Mrs Tait said, her eyes shining. "Their mum has promised sparklers outside afterwards. Then several of the Ranger guides have invited their family and friends. They should arrive in . . ." she consulted her watch ". . . half an hour. This Penny For The Guy competition seems to have caught their

Illustration by Marianne Vinge.

imagination. I believe one group is making a life-size doll like Simon Cowell! I doubt we'll have any that actually look like Guy Fawkes." Her eyes crinkled at the corner.

"How much does it cost to enter?" Georgia hadn't asked Penelope for extra money, so it couldn't have been expensive.

"Five pounds," Mrs Tait replied. "That may sound a lot, but all of them are doing it in teams, so they can spread the fee amongst them. I do hope the evening raises a good amount for Prickles Hospital. Those hedgehogs need an endless supply of food, medical treatments and bandages." She shook her head. "Apparently the hedgehog is a very accident-prone animal, what with falling down drains and eating slug pellets. I just hope people check their bonfires before lighting them this week. Each year a number of hedgehogs get caught in the flames!"

A T that moment a well-built, tanned man, with swept-back dark hair walked in. He was carrying a black plastic bin bag and gave Mrs Tait a crooked smile.

"Hope I'm not too late," he said and put the bag on the floor.

"Oh, Mr Ashton, how helpful. Thank you so much." Mrs Tait's cheeks tinged pink. "Your mother . . . is she still sure?"

151

Mr Ashton nodded.

"Dad's been gone almost a year now and, well, these are mostly his older gardening clothes. I thought they'd be great for the girls, if any are stuck for outfits to make their guys." He pulled out a pile of newspapers as well. "You wanted these for them to use to make the guys, too?"

Mrs Tait nodded.

"They'll come in handy for stuffing trousers, so that they look like proper legs."

Mr Ashton noticed Penelope staring at him, and gave another of those crooked smiles.

Now it was her turn to blush. What a striking man! Not so much because of his friendly face or nice leather jacket, but his manner and gentle tones. He reminded her of a character out of an Enid Blyton book. Clean-looking and clean-living; a person you could trust. Not that real-life often reflected fiction, she told herself, but still . . .

He put the newspapers on a nearby table, took an old jumper out of the bag and ran a hand over its surface. Poor man. It was hard losing a parent. A lump formed in Penelope's throat. Six years on, she still missed her mum's hugs.

"But how rude of me," Mrs Tait cried. "Mrs Jones, this is Mr Ashton – my neighbour's son. A very helpful person to know. Only last week he mended my tumble-dryer. It would have cost me a fortune to call out a handyman!"

DESPITE her thumping heart Penelope managed a smile and did her best to ignore Georgia. Her daughter was looking at her from the other side of the room, with one eyebrow raised. This usually preceded a giggle.

"Nice to meet you," Penelope stuttered. "I'm sorry about your dad."

His eyes dulled for a second, then Mr Ashton put the jumper back in the bag.

"Thank you. It came as a shock, but Mum and I are slowly coming to terms to life without him."

Penelope nodded. Divorce wasn't completely unlike bereavement. When John's company had offered him a job in Scotland, the decision magnified how much the couple had grown apart. So he moved up there, the two of them assuring each other that she – and Georgia – would follow eventually. But then John had met Sylvia . . .

Penelope bit her lip. Despite everything she still missed his silly one-liners. At least they had remained civil, and Georgia happily spent most of her holidays up in the Highlands.

"Who is he?" Georgia whispered, sidling up whilst Mr Ashton helped the Ranger leader set out more tables and chairs.

"A friend of Mrs Tait. He's brought some spare clothes for the competition," Penelope explained.

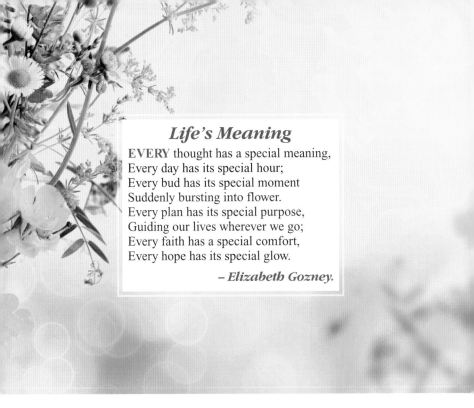

Life's Meaning

EVERY thought has a special meaning,
Every day has its special hour;
Every bud has its special moment
Suddenly bursting into flower.
Every plan has its special purpose,
Guiding our lives wherever we go;
Every faith has a special comfort,
Every hope has its special glow.

– Elizabeth Gozney.

Georgia's eyes shone.

"What?" Penelope asked with indignation.

"Nothing." Georgia stared at her mum for a moment before giving her a quick kiss. "I'm glad you're here. You don't get out enough."

And then she was gone, with the carefree skip of a young girl, having spotted some sixth-form friends who'd just turned up at the door.

Penelope felt proud. It was over two years since John had left and she'd been blessed with an unselfish daughter who, for the most part, understood that divorce wasn't just hard on the children. In fact, she'd been hinting lately that it might be nice if Penelope met a new partner.

"Lucy's mum tried that internet dating," Georgia had said last week. "I could help you set up a profile, if you like."

"That's not for me!" Penelope had protested.

"But it's the modern way, Mum," all-knowing Georgia replied with a serious expression.

Eventually Penelope had agreed, but had given up after a string of unsuccessful dates.

"Lucy's mum says the virtual world of dating is just like the real one," Georgia said. "You need a bit of patience."

Penelope had shrugged and deleted her profile, not wanting to tell Georgia

the reason why so many dates had ended on a flat note. Several of the men she'd met hadn't wanted a ready-made family. One mention of her daughter, often brought a date to its end.

With a mental shake, Penelope put her negative thoughts to one side and helped set out the food and drinks. Then she supervised some of the teams, putting forward ideas for their guys, although the youngsters had plenty of sensible suggestions of their own.

"I'll have one of those chocolate cupcakes, please," Mr Ashton requested just before the winner was about to be announced. He'd stayed to help make the newspaper dolls. He took a fifty pence piece from his wallet. With a grin he held it out.

"Home-baking is a real treat for me." Mr Ashton then proceeded to reveal to her his failed attempts over the years at getting sponges to rise or biscuits not to burn. "But I do make a mean casserole," he finished. "And, funnily enough, a decent Yorkshire pudding."

"My batter always goes gloopy, so I usually buy frozen ones," Penelope put in.

"I buy ready-made cakes. Thank goodness for convenience food, otherwise my sweet tooth would never be satisfied."

They smiled at each other and for a moment stood in a comfortable silence.

"The evening's been a great success, hasn't it?" Penelope said eventually. "A really good turn-out."

He nodded.

"Mrs Tait is a lovely lady. Always inviting my mum round for a coffee, or helping her with the garden."

Penelope's brow furrowed as she puzzled over this.

"Mum had a hip replacement not long before Dad died," he explained. "Mrs Tait has been a life-saver. Sadly, my fingers aren't the slightest bit green."

"Mine, neither." Penelope laughed. "In fact, if it wasn't so expensive I'd have Astroturf fitted."

Mr Ashton chuckled.

"Have you visited that new garden centre off Hallam Road roundabout? I went in to buy some flowers for Mum. You can buy artificial ivy to trail across sheds and multi-coloured plastic flowers."

"Shh!" Her eyes twinkling, Penelope put a finger to her lips. "Don't let animal-lover Mrs Tait hear you. I don't think she'd approve, as buying those wouldn't help the dwindling bee population."

The two of them grinned and Mr Ashton bit into the cupcake.

"Although she would have a point – almost everyone in our road has replaced their front lawns with tarmac," Penelope went on. "I was wondering, next summer, whether to have a go at planting some flower-beds."

Gardening had been John's strong point, and Georgia never ceased to giggle at her mum's ability to over-water a houseplant.

"There's an evening course starting soon at that college on Marple Street," Mr Ashton said. He took out a handkerchief and wiped his mouth. "I was thinking of enrolling. Forms don't have to be handed in until next Friday. Perhaps you might . . ."

"My daughter goes to the sixth form there," Penelope told him.

"Ah." Mr Ashton stared at her for a moment before clearing his throat. "Excuse me a minute, Mrs Jones. I've just seen someone I know from the squash club."

And with that he was gone.

Penelope's stomach scrunched. Surely he had been just about to suggest she accompany him on this course, until he had found out about Georgia? Yet he'd seemed so different from the other men she'd met – easy to talk to and, most importantly, able to laugh at himself.

With a sigh, she busied herself clearing away empty plastic cups and plates. As Penelope wandered near Mr Ashton to pick up some empty cupcake cases, she couldn't help overhearing his conversation with his squash club friend.

Mr Ashton was shaking his head.

"Honestly," he said, "anyone would have to be mad to work with children."

Her mouth set in a firm line, Penelope carried on clearing. Obviously tonight wasn't the night she'd meet a special someone.

THE winner of the Guy Fawkes competition was about to be announced. Penelope forced a smile on her face and gave a thumbs-up sign across the room to Georgia. Mother and daughter – both with their blonde hair and hazel eyes – were a package, and any man who didn't understand that wasn't the man for her.

"And the winner is . . ." Mrs Tait began several minutes later ". . . the Goth guy! I love his black wig, and that black suit was a real find from the charity shop."

A group of teenagers whooped and clapped and Penelope couldn't help smiling.

"A deserving winner," a soft voice said beside her. It was Mr Ashton. "Although I am surprised Mrs Tait chose such a menacing entrant! I thought she'd prefer the guy dressed up like Worzel Gummidge."

Penelope shrugged.

"People don't always behave as you'd expect."

At that moment Georgia bounced over.

"Aw, my team lost, Mum."

"Never mind, it's the taking part that counts."

Georgia rolled her eyes.

"Do parents ever stop saying that?" She smiled at Mr Ashton. "Or teachers?"

Penelope blinked.

"Didn't you know, Mum?" Georgia shrugged. "Lucy just told me – this is Mr Ashton. He teaches her little sister." Georgia smiled at Mr Ashton. "You work at Beechlands Infants school, don't you?"

"Oh! I thought . . ." Penelope's cheeks tinged pink.

Mr Ashton nodded.

"Yes, and I was just saying to my friend, Jack, that you have to be mad to want to work with children! All day yesterday they were chattering about Bonfire Night instead of getting on with their work, having only recently got over the excitement of Hallowe'en." His eyes shone. "The little scamps! Not that I'd have it any other way. They soon grow out of that innocent excitement about simple things."

"Not Georgia. You should have seen her last week, dressed up as a pumpkin!"

"Mum!" Georgia hissed, but there was a twinkle in her eyes as she went back to her friends.

"I tried growing a pumpkin once," Mr Ashton admitted. "It looked more like an orange."

He cleared his throat.

"Mrs Jones, I was going to ask you to join me on that gardening course, but . . ." He flushed.

"What?" Penelope's heart raced.

"I wasn't sure what your husband might think. I mean, when you mentioned your daughter, it reminded me that I can't go asking out married women!"

Her eyes crinkled.

"My husband – or rather ex-husband – and I are divorced. I just haven't changed my name. I forget that people must assume I'm still married."

His face brightened.

"Oh! So . . .?"

She nodded.

"I would love to learn more about gardening."

"Great! If you like I'll give you my phone number."

She nodded again. Normally she wouldn't take contact details without knowing a man better, but she trusted Mrs Tait as a judge of character.

"I'm Guy, by the way," he said with a broad smile.

"And I'm Penelope, but friends call me Penny," she said. After a quick glance at each other, the couple burst out laughing.

"What's so funny?" Georgia asked, appearing and eyeing them suspiciously.

"Let's just say there might be more than one winner this year in the Penny For The Guy competition – and that could be me." Mr Ashton chuckled at Georgia's puzzled face, whilst fireworks crackled in the background.

Maybe, just maybe, this was the friendship Penny had been waiting for. ▪

First Class

by Anne Pack.

Illustration by Mike Heslop.

THAT'S the last of the strong brown tape, and I've still got three boxes to seal!" Hayley wailed.

She put her hands on her hips and looked around with a frown at the growing pile of cardboard boxes in the sitting-room.

"I'm sure there's a roll in the junk drawer in the hall!" Gill shouted from upstairs.

"Great, thanks, Mum." Hayley jumped to her feet. "At this rate I won't have the strength to unpack at the other end. I feel like I've been up all night."

"I'm sure you'll have a sudden burst of energy when you get into your cottage. It's all very exciting," Gill said, descending the stairs with two big suitcases.

"I suppose so." Hayley broke off a piece of tape with her teeth. "I just wish I was there and unpacked. It's not only my clothes and personal belongings, but all my work stuff that's creating the extra effort."

"Look upon that as a blessing. It means you have a job and you're your own boss. Coffee?"

"Oh, yes, please. I need something to keep me awake for the rest of the day. Where's Dad?"

"He's just gone to collect the hire van. Between us we'll get it packed in no time and be on our way."

Hayley sat at the kitchen table and traced the oak grain with her finger.

157

Gill put her hand on top of her daughter's.

"You've done that ever since you were a little girl, any time you're worried or nervous about something. This is a new chapter in your life. Aunt Chrissie thought a lot of you."

"I miss her," Hayley said, sipping her coffee. "It will seem strange living in her cottage without her in it."

"She was born in that cottage. She always felt she'd done my mother out of her rightful inheritance by remaining single and staying on after their parents died."

"So you think she left it to me out of guilt?" Hayley didn't like the thought of that.

"Oh, no. Aunt Chrissie always had a soft spot for you. Even when you were a child she hinted that one day you'd have the cottage. Here's your dad now." Gill reached for the coffee pot and poured a third cup.

"I smell coffee," Rod said, closing the door behind him. "All packed?"

He mischievously put his hands on the sides of Hayley's face.

"Dad! You're freezing!" Hayley cried, jumping up and spilling coffee on her jeans.

"You're telling me. It must be minus two out there. It'll be even colder in Greenside. It's completely exposed with absolutely no protection."

"But when the sun shines it's the perfect place to be," Gill replied. "Now, drink your coffee. The quicker we get started, the sooner we'll get finished."

THE best thing Aunt Chrissie did was to have this log burner installed," Rod said, locking the glass door on the big log he'd just added to the flames.

"The damp smell is disappearing," Hayley commented, cheered by the prospect.

"I told you it would. Just keep the fire topped up, and make sure you refill the basket from the log store regularly. You never know when the weather is going to turn."

"Come on, Hayley," Gill said, raising an eyebrow at her husband. "Let's get your work room organised."

The 19th-century cottage was at the end of a farm road. Chrissie's dad had worked on the farm and had been given the deeds to the house on retirement in gratitude for a lifetime of service. Hayley loved sitting in front of the fire as a child, listening to Chrissie's stories about a life that seemed too hard to be real. The valley was dotted with such workers' cottages, mostly now weekend retreats or holiday homes.

Later, Hayley dozily watched the flames curl round the logs as she sipped her hot chocolate. Chrissie's big armchair was surprisingly comfortable.

She pulled her feet under her and laid her head back as memories flooded her mind. Childhood holidays and day visits were eagerly looked forward to, with expeditions to the woods and on to the moor, all the while learning about nature. The cottage had a good-sized garden in which Chrissie had grown vegetables and fruit.

"Old habits die hard," Chrissie had said to Hayley when she'd asked why she didn't just buy them in the supermarket like everyone else.

Chrissie had steadfastly refused to move to sheltered accommodation in the nearby village, arguing that as long as she could remain independent she'd live in her cottage. Her passing of a heart attack came out of the blue, just before her eightieth birthday.

Despite her misgivings earlier in the day, Hayley had a good feeling about this move. It was a fresh start after her romance with Steve had fizzled out. It was one thing studying the same subjects together at college, but Steve's move to Manchester to work for a graphics company had sealed the end of the relationship.

Hayley had buried herself in her work and built up her online business, working long hours to meet demand. She had also walked the streets with samples of her accessories, and managed to get a few independent shops to take some on a sale or return basis. Her parents told her she needed a better work/life balance, so when Hayley learned that she had inherited the cottage, they had wasted no time in helping her to prepare for the move, saying the independence would do her good. Hayley agreed, and had mentally begun to make a work plan with built-in leisure time.

HAYLEY'S eyes peeped out over the woollen scarf that was wrapped round her neck and face several times, her nose wet with vapour from her breath. She made her way into the village like she had done every other day since moving two months previously. Recently, there had been a flurry of orders thanks to an old-stock sale and Hayley was evenly balanced by a big carrier bag in each hand. She skirted round the icy patches underfoot. Frost twinkled in the hedgerows and trees, and wisps of smoke spiralled from chimneys, reaffirming her belief that it had been a good decision to move to the pretty village.

The locals knew Hayley through her visits to Chrissie over the years and she was welcomed with open arms by everyone. Typical examples were George and Meg.

"It's lovely to know that you're here to stay," George said as he leaned on his walking stick.

"Yes, it is," Meg agreed, putting her hand on Hayley's arm. "It's so nice that Chrissie's house is staying in the family. Maybe you'll settle here, get married and have children. The primary school needs a regular new intake if it is to stay open."

No pressure then, Hayley thought.

"Pay no heed, Hayley. It's lovely to have you among us."

Reaching her destination, the sub post office, Hayley turned the brass handle and pushed. The door refused to open so she took her glove off, thinking it might be slipping, but no, the door was firmly locked. Hayley checked her watch. With furrowed brows she read the time: five past ten.

Fleeting annoyance quickly gave way to the thought that old Mrs Davidson might be ill. Panic-stricken, Hayley shielded her eyes against the winter glare and peered in the window. There was no movement. She crouched down and pushed open the letter-box.

"Mrs Davidson, are you there?"

Silence. Hayley stamped her feet on the ground, the coldness seeping through her thick-soled boots. She tried again, a bit louder this time.

"Mrs Davidson, can you hear me?" Suddenly the door flew open and Hayley overbalanced, landing face first on to a pair of slippered feet.

"My, my, we're keen this morning."

Hayley took the outstretched hand which easily pulled her to stand, and found herself face to face with a midnight-shadowed, tousle-haired young man with smiling hazel eyes.

"Mrs Davidson?"

"No, it's Rob, actually," he said, pointing to the name badge, which Hayley noticed was on upside-down.

"I mean, where is Mrs Davidson?"

"I'm afraid she had a little turn last night. Nothing serious, I'm told, but she's been taken into hospital as a precaution. I'm covering counter duties meantime."

"Oh, poor Mrs Davidson. I hope she recovers soon."

"We've only just met. Do you want rid of me so soon?" Rob turned his head sideways and gave a feigned hurt look.

"Mrs Davidson is in hospital, and you're making a joke about it," Hayley replied, irritated at his flippancy.

"I'm sorry. I sometimes say things before I think. Here, let me relieve you of these heavy bags, and come in out of the cold. You must be frozen."

It was important to Hayley that her order made the morning post to arrive by the promised date. She didn't want any negative reviews on her website. To save costs she always sent mail second class. She glanced up at the wall clock.

"I'll be open on time tomorrow," Rob promised with a grin. "I only got the call at eight o'clock this morning, and had just enough time to stuff a few things in a bag."

With numbed fingers Hayley lifted the parcels out of the bags and put

Our Old Car

OUR car will soon be destined
For the scrap yard in the sky.
I'm really going to miss her
When we've said our last goodbye.
She's served us well for many years,
She's taken us around
To local shops and holidays,
She's rarely let us down.
She's been on all the school runs,
To theatre and to show.

She's there in all our memories –
I can't bear to let her go.
Her seats have had their share of crisps,
Of jam and lemonade;
The floor is full of papers
And things that we've mislaid.
Then suddenly I have a thought
As I wipe away a tear –
Perhaps we could repair her, so
She'll last another year!

– Eliza Barret.

them on the scales one by one.

"First or second?" Rob asked pleasantly.

"Second, and can I have a receipt?"

"Of course. A business, is it?"

"Yes, it is."

Rob seemed to be so preoccupied with searching around the little office for things that Hayley decided not to go into detail. He knocked over the scales, dropped the stamp book, and tripped over a bag of mail.

"I'll be with you shortly," he called over Hayley's shoulder to the growing queue. "Just as soon as I've finished with this lovely young lady."

Hayley knew her nose was already red, but felt a flush spread over her face. She regretted she hadn't taken time to put some make-up on.

"She is lovely, isn't she?"

Hayley swung round to see a smiling George and two other villagers, nodding in assent.

"It's a cold morning, Hayley. Why don't you pop in for a cuppa with me and Meg before you head home."

"That would be lovely, George, thank you." It had been an odd start to the day. A bit of normality was just the ticket before she began her day's work.

HI, Mum. Yes, everything's OK, thanks." It was unusual for Gill to phone midweek. Normally they caught up by e-mail every evening and exchanged visits at least once a week. "Is everything all right with you and Dad?"

"Oh, yes, your dad's gone out for a pint with his friends so I thought I'd give you a ring. The weather's turning nasty. I wanted to make sure you were prepared for it. There's snow forecast and we might not be able to get to you. I remember Aunt Chrissie being cut off for days at a time."

"I've got plenty food in, and thanks to Dad I've enough logs to last for months. Everyone's being really nice – I won't be stuck for anything."

"That's good. How's Mrs Davidson?"

"She's still in hospital. She should be discharged this week. Wait a minute – I never told you she was ill. How did you know?"

Hayley hadn't mentioned it because she didn't want to talk about Rob, who she had seen many times since the morning she so embarrassingly fell at his feet. To be fair, the post office had opened on time every day since, but Rob clearly didn't have the same sleek efficiency as Mrs Davidson. The clumsiness he'd displayed on the first day was obviously more to do with him than the unfamiliarity of his surroundings. Hayley found it highly amusing, and couldn't contain her laughter the day his hands got covered in ink from the stamping pad.

"George rang me. He was my informant during Aunt Chrissie's time. He also mentioned the temp was a rather good-looking young man who had taken a fancy to you."

"That's not true," Hayley said, louder than she'd meant.

But it was true, and Hayley knew it. If Rob needed to know local information he'd pop next door to ask George, and in return Rob helped George with a computer problem. One day Rob had confided that he would like to ask Hayley out, but was afraid she'd turn him down. George had wasted no time in relaying this information to Hayley, and she began to see Rob in a different light.

She noticed that he was patient and kind to the elderly customers, offering his help with form-filling, or finding an address. He'd rush to help Hayley when she saw her approach with bulky parcels. He'd barge his way to the counter with them, often knocking the stands of greetings cards over. She noticed, too, how good-looking he was, especially when he smiled, and she was aware that she took time to put make-up on before every visit.

Orders were flying in thick and fast, keeping Hayley fully occupied, and making daily trips to the post office. It had been a good thing to decide on tweeds and plaids, she reasoned, despite the warnings of those supposedly in the know.

"It's too old-fashioned – it'll never take off," one of her lecturers said. But Hayley had set her mind on it, because it was different from what anyone else was doing. She had made a few sample purses, handbags and brooches, which sold out immediately at a craft fayre, and it escalated from there. Hayley wished her lecturers could see her now. Her mind was brimming with ideas and she regularly introduced new items to the collection, such as teddies, door stops and picture frames. Even Rob had commented on it.

"Very impressive website. I had a look last night." His eyes narrowed at the gauge on the scales. "First or second?" He knew the answer, but he had to ask.

"Second, and thanks for the comments. A friend from college built the site for me at mate's rates."

"I'd like to hear more about it. Do you have time for a cuppa this morning? Though you'd have to put up with me rushing through to the shop every time the bell rang?"

"Sure, why not."

Hayley was mindful of Rob's fear of rejection, but even so, she didn't want to seem too keen, even though her heart was doing somersaults. Settling herself in a seat by the fire, she took the mug from Rob. She realised she knew very little about him.

"Where are you from, Rob?" It was a feeble question.

"I'm not sure, to be honest."

Hayley wasn't surprised at this vague answer. She was used to Rob blurting out what he thought or felt without engaging his brain first.

"Dad was in the Army so we moved around. I'd just get used to a place, and we'd move again. I don't know where I class as home. I went to university in London, graduated and got a job with the post office. I just go where I'm needed, but I live in Hackleigh Heath at the other side of the moor. I can cover quite a distance to work in every direction. How's your coffee?"

"Lovely, thanks." But the company was even better, Hayley thought.

After all the stilted conversations across the counter, today's flowed easily and things were going so well she was sure he was going to ask her out on a date. But every time the conversation reached a possible point for doing so, the shop bell rang. After the umpteenth time she knew she

Secrets

SECRETS are hosts of small signs one
    might miss,
Like a wink, or a smile, or a brief,
    discreet kiss.
A secret is something that stands quite
    alone
In the mind of one person to whom it
    is known.
It might be a language, a symbol or sign,
Encrypted with skill in a special design;
It might be a place, a passage or room,
A tune that is played, or a rare
    nom de plume.
It could be a wish, a password or plan,
Devised by the will of an ordinary man.
But should it be now or a hundred
    years old,
A secret's a thing that can never be told.

– Dawn Lawrence.

shouldn't stay any longer.

"Thanks for the coffee," Hayley said as she made her way through the post office.

"You're welcome. We must do it again."

"Yes, we must."

Hayley floated on air as she made her way home.

NEXT morning, Hayley pulled the curtain back to a blinding blanket of snow. Only the top half of the gate posts were showing and when she opened the front door a wall of snow met her.

It became quickly apparent that there was also a power cut, so Hayley banked up the log burner from the groaning baskets of logs in the hearth, half-filled a pot with water and put it on top of the stove to boil, estimating in her head how many meals she could make this way. This independence wasn't so bad after all, Hayley surmised confidently.

Using candlelight to cut out fabric shapes, ready for machining when the power came back on, Hayley contentedly hummed to herself. Later, nestled in the armchair, she doodled in her sketch book, designing ear-muffs, head bands and scarves, inspired by the swirling snow outside.

But by the following day the log pile was dwindling alarmingly fast, she was almost out of fresh milk and her mobile phone was out of charge. The little battery-operated radio was her only contact with the outside world and the forecast wasn't good. Snow and low temperatures were set to continue for another 24 hours.

Hayley eked out the logs and next morning used the big plastic snow spade her dad had left, inside the back door, to dig a path to the log store. Half an hour later, and with frozen hands and feet, she carried armfuls of logs and filled the baskets beside the fire, piling more around the hearth. Shivering from cold, she found self-pity began to set in.

"Stop being such a baby," Hayley remonstrated with herself through her tears. "You're being ridiculous. George and Meg will be in the same boat. So will Rob."

How she wished she was safe and warm beside his fireside.

Resolutely, she wrapped up with dry outer clothes and tackled the front path. It was slow going, but aided by the winter sun which was melting the snow, the job was made easier. An hour later, she'd made good progress.

As she straightened her aching back, she heard the welcome sound of a tractor. It was the farmer. He opened the window and shouted to Hayley that he'd clear the main road with the snow plough affixed to the tractor, then return to help her. This was music to her ears.

Not only did he return, but he brought an army of helpers with him, who made light work of clearing Hayley's path. Rob was one of them.

"Here, you might need these," he said, handing Hayley a box full of groceries.

He looked even more handsome with a beanie on his head, striped scarf, and rosy cheeks.

"Yes, I do, and thank you. I'm more grateful than you can imagine."

"It wasn't my idea. This village is amazing. Everyone's rallying round, making up boxes for people further down the valley. Said they're used to doing this."

"All the same, I'm so glad to see you all. If the power came back on it would be perfect."

"It's due to come back on soon. I'll call in later, if that's all right?"

"Yes, of course. I'd come, too, but I'm not sure I would be much use."

"You stay here and keep warm. Meg asked me to put in a flask of her home-made soup for you. Enjoy." Rob leaned forward unexpectedly and kissed Hayley on the lips. She closed her eyes but couldn't feel a thing. Her lips were frozen. She said so to Rob.

"Mine, too." He smiled. "When I come back later, we'll do it again – with feeling!"

They both dissolved in giggles at the thought.

B Y the time Rob returned the power was back on and Hayley was working on orders that had come in.

"Something smells good," Rob commented as he hung his coat in the hall. "Shepherd's pie?"

"Spot on," Hayley replied. "Two days of convenience food is enough for anyone. Mum made it – I took it out of the freezer earlier."

As Hayley and Rob sat either side of the log burner, with their food on a lap tray, Hayley couldn't remember feeling happier.

"Isn't it silly? I thought it would never stop snowing and I'd be stuck in this house for weeks!"

"You underestimated the power of good neighbours. George phoned me to check I was all right. Next thing I knew people were out with shovels, clearing paths. Bags and boxes were going from house to house. It's extraordinary."

"Any word on Mrs Davidson?" Hayley asked.

"Still in hospital. My manager told me she is giving up the post office and wants to move into sheltered housing in the village."

Hayley was relieved that Mrs Davidson was recovering and had decided to slow down.

"So what will happen with the post office?"

"It depends?"

"On what?"

"If my bid for taking it over is accepted. I submitted it last week. No-one else expressed interest so I'd say it's pretty certain."

"That's wonderful news!" This time Hayley didn't try to sound or act cool. She was delighted.

Rob put his tray in the kitchen and took Hayley's from her.

"Now, about that kiss?"

"What about it?" Hayley teased, looking up into Rob's smiling eyes.

Without another word he kissed Hayley softly on the lips.

As they sat snuggled up on the sofa watching the dancing flames, the constant drips of thawing snow and ice outside could be heard.

"Do you think you'll be happy living here?" Hayley asked. "It's a quirky little village."

"You're telling me. This is the first place in the whole of my life that I've felt I wanted to put roots down."

"Because of its quirkiness?"

"That, and the fact that I met a special someone who threw herself at my feet the very first time we met." ■

I'd Like To Know....

Sit back and enjoy this classic selection of vintage queries from the lovely readers of the "Friend"!

Q **AFTER** putting in my usual order for Christmas turkey at my local butcher's, I started to wonder exactly when it was that turkey became our traditional festive fare. Does eating turkey at Christmas go back to mediaeval times?

– Mrs L.E., Barry.

A **NO,** Mrs E., it does not. In fact, turkey as a Christmas meal is a relatively modern trend as it was a luxury right up until the 1950s, when refrigerators and freezers became more widely available. In mediaeval times, traditional Christmas fare included roast swan, pheasants and peacocks. A special treat was a roast boar's head decorated with holly and fruit.

Q **MY** mum mentioned going out with my dad to a British Restaurant during the war when they were courting. What exactly was a British Restaurant? My mum wasn't very sure.

– Mrs I.K., Doncaster.

A **BRITISH** Restaurants, or Community Feeding Centres, as they were originally called, were set up by the Ministry of Food and run by local communities on a non-profit-making basis during WWII. Meals were purchased for a set maximum price of 9d or less. No-one was allowed more than one serving of a meal that consisted of meat, game, poultry, fish, eggs or cheese. Restaurants were not subject to rationing, but some restrictions were placed upon them – no meal could be more than three courses and the maximum price for that was five shillings. By 1942 there were 1,899 British Restaurants in the London County Council area.

Q **IN** the 1950s there was a television show on every Saturday evening, "Six-Five Special". Can you settle an argument and tell me who sang the theme tune? Was it Marty Wilde or Don Lang?

– Mr J.L., Shipley.

A **THE** "Six-Five Special" was launched in February 1957 by the BBC at a time when both television and rock and roll were new to the UK. Don Lang and his Frantic Five were the resident band for the show and they sang the theme tune. Artists who appeared on the show included Petula Clark, Lonnie Donegan and Cleo Laine.

Thinkstockphotos.

167

He's Behind You!

by Christine Evans.

ARE you coming to the panto or not, Louise?" my mother asked. "Dunno," I said warily. "Is Dad going?"

"Of course he is," Mum replied in exasperation. "Auntie Dot is in it, after all. She's playing the fairy godmother. The family always support her."

Auntie Dot was the thespian in the family. She was a major player in our local amateur dramatic society, the Prestown Players, and always looked for support for her productions from the family. Dad had once been a member himself when he was younger and that's where he and Mum met. Auntie Dot was his sister.

When I was younger I'd joined in, too, playing various mice, urchins and village children. Then my little sister Lizzie had come along and Mum had had to give up helping out. Soon afterwards Dad started working shifts for more wages to keep our little family and he couldn't always go to rehearsals.

So Auntie Dot kept the family flag flying, though now Lizzie was older, Dad and Mum sometimes manned the ticket and programme sales to help out. We always went to the pantomime. This year it was "Cinderella".

There was no problem for me if the production was a play or a musical. Dad was quite happy applauding his sister and the rest of the cast. No, a major source of embarrassment for me was the annual pantomime. Dad loved pantos. He cheered, he called out the catchphrases with loud enthusiasm, he sang loudly (and slightly out of tune) whenever there was a chorus to sing. It hadn't bothered me until recently, but at the last performance I'd felt my face going hot and I fought a fierce urge to tell him to be quiet. He was a grown-up, for goodness' sake!

"He's behind you!" he'd yelled, to the delight of the little kids around him. Then they'd all joined in with him. They were so used to being told to be quiet whenever they went to the cinema or a theatre that they didn't always get the hang of a panto right away.

At the last pantomime I caught the eye of Amanda Purdy, from my class, along the row, and she gave a knowing and superior smirk. Amanda's oldest

Illustration by Jim Dewar/Thinkstockphotos.

sister, Chantelle, invariably played one of the leads. She was very pretty, though she didn't have a very strong voice and often sang off key. Now Amanda had noticed Dad's behaviour, I'd never felt so embarrassed in all my life.

Next day she was telling all the kids in my class how my dad was behaving, then Amanda and her gang took that as a cue to torment me.

"Oh, he's behind you!" they'd call whenever they happened to follow me down a corridor.

I tossed my hair and ignored them, as my friends Jessie and Kate advised me to, but it was still embarrassing.

So you can see I'd have to think carefully about my presence at the panto. I wondered if I could find out which day Amanda would be going. It only ran for three days. We usually went on a Friday. If I could persuade Mum to book for either of the other two days it might work out all right. I did enjoy pantos, and Auntie Dot had a lovely voice despite being a little plump for the lead parts.

There was another reason that I didn't want to be shown up in class. Jason Crosby had recently come to our school. All the girls liked him. He wasn't what you'd call pop star handsome, but he was tall and funny and a right laugh. I didn't tell my friends I liked him because they'd have teased me. Besides, I think Jessie and Kate fancied him, too, because I noticed they tried to look cool and nonchalant whenever he came near, just like I did. It would be so humiliating to have Amanda and her mates calling after me in school and for Jason to witness it.

I had a decision to make – should I go and miss out on all the fun, or stay at home and save myself from being teased in class?

"We'll probably be going on Friday night," my mother said.

"What about Thursday for a change?" I tried.

"But if we go on Thursday you and Lizzie will be in school next day and Dad and I will be in work." Mum was a teaching assistant in Lizzie's school. "If we go on Friday we can have a lie-in on Saturday morning," she said reasonably.

I was left with the prospect of either being embarrassed by my dad or not going at all.

"Please come," Lizzie coaxed.

Our Lizzie was a budding thespian herself. She was one of the first youngsters to dash up on stage when they asked for children to come up. One year she'd won a teddy bear for lisping through a song with her two front teeth missing and she was keen to repeat her performance.

"Please come, Lou," she pleaded again, with eyes like saucers. My little sister is a bit spoilt because she has the knack of coaxing us to do anything she wants by giving us her big-eyed Bambi look.

"All right," I said. "I'll come."

"Goody," Lizzie said, clapping her hands. "You can sit next to me."

So I was resigned to what would happen. Then I heard Amanda boasting about Chantelle playing the princess and that her family were going every night to see the panto at our local church hall. I couldn't have escaped her presence anyway.

There was another awful bit of news, too.

Trimming The Tree

IT'S time to fetch the Christmas decorations from the attic.
As I recall, they're shabby, and this year I'm quite emphatic:
We'll have the most sophisticated tree I've ever seen –
So stylish it could feature in a glossy magazine!

Which decorations ought to be replaced with something new?
I'll keep the stars the children made, although they hang askew.
Oh, look – the little stocking that was knitted by my gran;
And here's the pair of robins that we've had since time began!

This tinsel is unravelling; this bauble has a crack –
But they're my special favourites (I'll hang them round the back!)
The angel's slightly crooked and this rocking horse is bent;
Our snowman's lost his shimmer and the candle has a dent.

Garlands, lights and baubles – shining, iridescent spheres . . .
Trinkets that we've cherished and collected through the years.
They may not be perfect, but I love them all so much.
Stylish? No – but I think I prefer the homely touch!

– Emma Canning.

"Did you know Jason's going to be in that panto that your auntie Dot is in?" Jessie asked. "His dad's playing the king and he's a courtier or something like that. I think his mum's in it, too. I was behind him on the bus and he was telling his mate."

Knowing Jessie, she'd have deliberately sat behind Jason so she could ogle him. You could always rely on her to get the latest gossip, though my heart sank at the news. He would be there to see my dad's embarrassing behaviour at first hand.

"Do you think you could get me a ticket?" Kate asked, looking slightly embarrassed.

I just knew she wanted to drool over Jason. I'd wanted to do that by myself in the darkness of the church hall.

"I'd like to come, too, if you can get tickets," Jessie decided.

Neither of them had shown the slightest interest in my aunt's AmDram performances before, but I knew watching Jason perform was the big attraction for them. I promised I'd do what I could and secretly hoped there would be no tickets left. Unfortunately, Dad was only too delighted to support his sister's efforts and came home from Dot's with two more tickets for the panto. I was doomed!

O N the night of the performance I noticed Amanda sitting just ahead of my friends and me. Lizzie had seated herself conveniently in the middle of us in the hope of coaxing more sweets out of my friends. They thought my little sister was cute, but they hadn't realised yet what a spoilt madam she was. They'd soon find out after she'd wheedled away their sweets.

I thought Jason looked adorable in satin, though that wasn't something you'd admit to every day. I could see Jessie and Kate's eyes swivel towards him whenever he came on stage.

Then Dad began his performance.

"He's behind you!" he shouted as Buttons played tricks on the Ugly Sisters. The young ones in front giggled at a grown man acting daft, and then they joined in. Jessie and Kate's eyes widened in amazement at Dad's antics, but then they began to laugh and join in with the spirit of the panto, too. Soon everyone around us was acting like a bunch of noisy hecklers.

I could see Amanda's nose lifting in disdain. At least I wouldn't be alone when her cronies began taunting us at school.

Amanda's sister kept forgetting her lines and had to be prompted a few times. Then she sang one of her songs out of tune. Of course my eyes seemed to find Jason whenever I glanced at the stage and he seemed to be enjoying himself immensely. I idly wondered if Auntie Dot could get me a part in their next production.

The panto came to an end amid happy cheering (led by guess who!) and a rousing encore. I had enjoyed myself despite everything, and at least my friends had behaved as noisily as Dad. I had to admit I'd joined in, too.

"That was great," Kate said. "I haven't laughed so much in ages."

"It's nice to be daft once in a while," Jessie agreed, giggling. "Sometimes it's boring to be grown up."

"Jason did all right," I ventured.

"Yeah," they both said with a dreamy sigh.

My friends didn't seem to be the least embarrassed by Dad's behaviour, but then he wasn't their dad. Now all I had to do now was face the class on Monday.

The class were all sitting at their desks waiting for registration when I came in. I took a deep breath and glanced at Amanda. She was just about to say something snide when Jason jumped off his desk and came over.

"How did you enjoy the panto on Friday?" he asked, grinning.

"Yeah, it was all right," I said, trying to sound cool, although my heart was thumping. Then he said a surprising thing.

"Your dad was ace," he said with a beaming smile. "He really got the crowd going. It's great to have that audience participation when you're on stage. It gives you a boost. Your aunt Dot says she's always glad when he's in the audience as she knows we'll have a good response. She wishes he could come every night."

I stared at him in stunned silence.

"Yeah, some people don't bother to join in," Jason went on. "The whole point of a panto is to let your hair down and enjoy yourself, isn't it?"

"Yes," I said, smiling up at him in happy relief. "It is."

Amanda looked horrified.

"Dad used to be in the Prestown Players, too," I said.

"You should come along yourself," Jason said. "We have loads of fun."

"I might," I said casually, knowing full well that the next time they had a meeting I'd be there in the front row. "I used to be with the Players when I was younger."

"What did you do?"

So I told him about my mouse, urchin and villager career and he seemed impressed.

"I only joined recently," he said. "We always joined in the church panto each year where we used to live. When we moved here Mum thought it would be a good way of meeting people if we joined the local amateur dramatic society. She's made lots of friends."

"Well, I think I might come along," I said, trying to act cool. "Auntie Dot is always trying to get me to come back."

NOW I was very keen to do just that. I might end up as a spear carrier or a village maiden, but I was sure to have fun, not to mention the bonus of seeing more of Jason. I just knew I'd have been tongue-tied if he'd talked to me before, but now we had amateur dramatics to talk about, the conversation flowed naturally. Kate and Jessie and most of the girls in the class looked at me enviously. Amanda Purdy looked as if she would explode with jealousy.

Wasn't I glad that I'd gone to the panto after all! I'd discovered that, instead of being an embarrassment, my dad was a really good audience member to have. Who would have thought it?

Like my friend said, it's nice to be daft sometimes. ▓